THE SUNDAY TIMES
BOOK OF
Brain
Teasers

THE SUNDAY TIMES
BOOK OF
Brain Teasers

50 hard (<u>very</u> hard) master problems

Compiled and Edited by
Victor Bryant and Ronald Postill

St. Martin's Press
New York

St. Martin's Press titles are available at quantity discounts for
sales promotions, premiums or fund raising. Special books or
book excerpts can also be created to fit specific needs. For
information write to special sales manager, St. Martin's Press,
175 Fifth Avenue, New York, N.Y. 10010.

Mass market edition/April 1986

ISBN: 0-312-90338-3

First published in Great Britain by Unwin Paperbacks

Foreword

The Sunday Times Brain-teaser was introduced more than twenty years ago as a novel addition to the puzzle page published at holiday time. Popular from the start it soon appeared more frequently, in its own right, until on 26 February 1961 it became a numbered weekly feature.

Its readership range has become immense, spanning not only the British Isles but also more than seventy overseas states. Just how many readers try unsuccessfully to solve the problems can only be guessed but it has been estimated that in any year at least one hundred thousand readers have a go.

Successful competitors embrace all ages from eight years to almost a century and represent all walks of life from bright young scholars to High Court judges and world-famous professors, with the ratio of women, now about one in five, constantly rising.

The volume of entries is of course determined weekly by the degree of brain-teasing presented and extends from a small handful, with sometimes only one correct answer or none at all, to loads approaching four thousand when concessions are occasionally made for readers of modest mathematical ability.

This age-old self-engendered urge to solve complicated problems would however be unsatisfied but for the breed of self-appointed torturers, all *Sunday Times* readers, who exploit their craving by conceiving, composing and scrambling problems of those categories uniquely required for Brain-teasers.

These problem setters, men, women and youths, like the solvers, are wide ranging in status but united in their determination to baffle or bewilder their prey. Professionals and amateurs alike, their work displays much variety of method and style and the present collection forms a fair and fascinating cross-section of the whole.

To this end the delicate task of selecting and compiling one hundred and one representative problems from those published in *The Sunday Times* in the last few years has been entrusted to two of the most regular and popular

Foreword – *continued*

practitioners of the pastime: Dr Victor Bryant, Lecturer in Pure Mathematics at the University of Sheffield, and Ronald Postill, Headmaster of Victoria College, Jersey, 1946–67; now Tutor for Admissions at Millfield School.

The happy result is two collections of fifty and fifty-one master problems calculated to give the requisite blend of pain and pleasure for many days to come.

ANTHONY FRENCH
Brain-teaser Editor
The Sunday Times

Introduction

This is the first of two books which include Brain-teasers largely chosen from those published in *The Sunday Times* during the six-year period from January 1974 to December 1979; and we thank that newspaper for its kind permission to reproduce the puzzles here. This selection of fifty Brain-teasers has been made to provide a variety of styles and of difficulties, and we hope that there is plenty here to please puzzlers of all tastes and abilities, although of course there are many excellent puzzles which we have been unable to include.

Reading through the Brain-teasers and the resulting correspondence from the files of *The Sunday Times*, it was immediately clear to us that the Brain-teaser column is held in some affection by both its organisers and its readers. The organisation is in the capable hands of Anthony French, and we take this opportunity to thank him for his efficient running of the column over the years and for his great help in the preparation of this book. The enthusiasm from the readers is clear from their short comments on the postcard entries: 'Highly ingenious', 'Phew', 'How *do* they think of them?' being fairly typical. In addition to the postcards, long and interesting analyses of the puzzles follow by letter, sometimes finding a flaw, but more often missing some subtle intention of the author. Seasoned puzzlers seem to get as much pleasure from finding a mistake as they do from finding an answer. In some cases we have made slight changes to the teasers (or to their solutions, which are to be found at the back of the book) in the light of letters received after their original publication. If any flaws remain (or indeed if we have introduced any by these changes) then the responsibility is ours.

The beauty of Brain-teasers is that they are set by a wide variety of authors, ranging from the prolific regulars to those individuals who have a single inspired idea. It is this variety which maintains the constant freshness of the column, and it is this variety which we hope to have captured in our selection.

VICTOR BRYANT
RONALD POSTILL

CONTENTS

THE BRAIN-TEASERS

Authors of Brain-teasers often notice odd coincidences around them, or imagine how day-to-day incidents can form the basis of a pleasant puzzle. Our first four choices are of this nature.

1 | *Pity the Postman*

Extract (genuine!) from a national daily Jan. 27, 1977:

'Pity the poor postman trying to deliver letters along Stonebow Road in the village of Drake's Broughton, in north-west England. Due to local government confusion the road boasts five houses with the number 1, four others are number 2, three have number 4, and two are numbered 6.

'To add to the postman's woes there are four families called Davies in Stonebow Road, plus two named Bridges, three named Barker, and two named Webb.'

On the unwarranted supposition that (i) the occupants of the said houses included all of the said families; but (ii) the postman's problem was somewhat alleviated by the fact that no two families of the same name had the same house-number; and (iii) the house-numbers of the Webbs totalled to more than did those of the Bridges, while those of all the families with two of the four names totalled the same as did those of all the families with the other two names:

What were the house-numbers of the Barkers and Webbs respectively **?**

Last week's Top Ten consisted of the following performers:

1 Adda
2 Bay Leaf Rissolers
3 Cate Gooseberry
4 Demi-Sour
5 Englebert Smith
6 Fatherhood of Man
7 Gee-Bees
8 How
9 It
10 John Revolter

This week the same ten were in the charts, but all their placings were different. Five had gone up and five had gone down. Adda had the biggest single drop of all, but Fatherhood went up.

When I looked at the products of last week's and this week's placings, I found that

(a) Gee-Bees' product was three times Cate Gooseberry's,
(b) It's was three times Demi-Sour's,
(c) Englebert's was even,
(d) The total of the products was 272.

What was this week's order **?**

3 | *Miss Brain-Teaser*

Five girls entered our Village Beauty Contest. Each of the five judges had to put them into a definite order and then allot fifteen marks between them. The aggregate marks for each girl decided the issue. The judges each gave a different maximum mark and also chose a different girl to be top. No girl had two identical marks in her score.

Joe gave the maximum possible to Rose and he placed Gwen above Linda. Tom gave Ann one more than Sam did. Pam had no zero in her score and although she finished ahead of Rose she didn't win. Ann scored the only five that was allotted. Dan placed the girls as closely together as he could.

The judge who put Gwen first put Rose last. Brian succeeded in putting them all in their correct final order.

Who won, and what were her individual marks from each judge ?

Newtown High Street has a linked traffic light system which consists of six consecutive sections, each a multiple of one-eighth of a mile, and each terminating in a traffic light.

The lights are synchronised such that a vehicle travelling at 30 mph will pass each light at the same point in its 26-second operating cycle.

This cycle can be considered as 13 seconds 'stop' (red) and 13 seconds 'go' (green).

Charlie had studied the system and reckoned he could drive much faster than 30 mph and still get through the system without crossing a red light.

In an experiment Alf, Bert and Charlie entered the first section at the same instant, travelling at 30, 50 and 75 mph respectively, with the first light turning green three seconds later.

Charlie got through the whole system in less than two minutes without being stopped.

'I was lucky though,' said Charlie. 'I arrived at the last light just as it changed.'

'My luck was non-existent,' said Bert. 'I ran out of petrol after the third light and in any case would have been stopped at the second light had I not lost 10 seconds due to a delay in the second section.'

What were the lengths of each section in order from the first **?**

Apart from being motivated by
everyday incidents such as those,
some teasers are based on some
extraordinary occurrences of
numbers in most natural ways.
The next puzzle, for example, is
apparently devoid of numbers
and yet it produces a numerical
and rather unexpected answer.
The next trio of puzzles all make
the most of our rather eccentric
method of measuring time.

Today a great celebration will take place on Bells Island, for it is the Feast of Coincidus. On this island there is a monastery and a nunnery. At regular intervals (a whole number of minutes) the monastery bell dongs once. The nunnery bell rings at regular intervals too (different from the intervals of the monastery's bell, but also a whole number of minutes). So the island also regularly reverberates with a ding from the nunnery's bell. The Feast of Coincidus takes place whenever the monastery's dong and the nunnery's ding occur at the same moment, and that is exactly what is due to happen at noon today.

Between consecutive Feasts the dongs from the monastery and the dings from the nunnery occur alternately and, although the two noises only coincide on Feast days, they do occur a minute apart at some other times.

When the bells coincided last time (at noon, a prime number of days ago) this whole island indulged in its usual orgy of eating and drinking.

How many days ago was that ?

Waking in the night I glanced at my bed-side clock and thought it indicated just after 2.20. Putting on my spectacles and looking more carefully I saw that it was actually just after 4.10. I had, of course, interchanged the hands at my first glance.

I began to wonder what time around then that my observation would have occurred, to the exact fraction of a minute, if the hands could have been exactly interchanged.

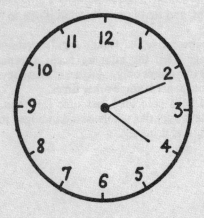

What do you think ?

Our old watchmaker works weekdays 9.30 am to 5 pm as regular as, well, clockwork. I recently took there to be regulated two '8-day' striking clocks – the sort which fully-wound will go nearly 8 days before stopping; they were keeping different times and each was wrong by an exact number of minutes per day, i.e. less than an hour in either case.

He immediately wound the clocks fully, set them to the right time (which was an exact number of minutes after the hour) and put them up on a shelf for observation.

The next Monday, when he went to take down the clocks to start regulating them, he found both of them just starting to strike 8 o'clock simultaneously, which was some hours plus an exact number of minutes past the correct time.

What day and exact time was it when he originally set them **?**

As we have already seen, puzzlers are attracted to prime numbers. Continuing our theme of teasers based on time, here are two 'prime' examples of the use of the calendar.

8 | *Old Father Prime*

Albert Prime will be joining us again today* for the 15th celebration of the anniversary of his birth since he was home on leave during the 1914-18 war.

On that occasion, his son David's age plus his brother Bert's age was equal to his brother Charlie's age; Bert's age plus Charlie's age was equal to Albert's age.

All the ages except Albert's were prime numbers and Albert's was the cube of David's. All four were born on 29th February in different years and the ages above are taken by counting how many 29th Februarys they have celebrated (for example, a man born on 29th February 1956 has an age of 3 today*).

In what year was Albert born ?

9 | *Prime Birthdays*

At our local the other night I made the acquaintance of a chap called Michael and his wife Noelle. We talked a good bit about our respective families, our activities and our hobbies. When I happened to mention my interest in mathematical puzzles to Michael he said that he knew one at first hand which might give me some amusement. He proceeded to tell me that although he himself, his parents (who were born in different years), Noelle and their children (featuring no twins, triplets, etc) had all been born in the nineteen-hundreds and none of them in a leap year, the numerical relationship between their years of birth was nevertheless in two respects a bit unusual.

'In the first place,' he said, 'just one of us has our year of birth precisely equal to the mean of all the others' years of birth. But more remarkably the difference between my father's year of birth and that of any one of the rest of us is a prime, and the same is true of that of my mother. And she, like Noelle here, had no child after she had passed her twenties.' And then with a grin he concluded 'So now you'll know about the whole family and even, if you want, be able to figure out just how old Noelle is without having to be rude and ask her!'

In which year was Noelle born, and how many children does she have **?**

Of course, teasers based on everyday measuring systems need not be restricted to the clock or calendar. But those based on money soon date due to inflation. Even so, we include two based on the postal rates of yesteryear.

Post Office multi-value coil machines are designed to vend strips of five stamps. Soon after the introduction of the 8½p and 6½p first and second class postal rates the machines sold for 10p a strip of stamps values 6p, 1p, ½p, 2p and ½p respectively (as always with these machines the last stamp being the lowest in case of tearing). While catering for both rates it was impossible to make up either 6½p or 8½p with a joined strip of stamps.

However an efficiency expert worked out a possible 10p strip which afforded the following:

  (i)   from one strip either first or second rate in a joined strip;

 (ii)   from two joined strips, three second class rates, each in a joined strip;

(iii)   from three joined strips, two first class rates plus two second class rates, each in a joined strip.

Of course the 'expert' assumed that all ½p steps from ½p to 10p were available in stamps.

What was his suggested strip   **?**

11 | Those Were the Days!

I went to the Post Office to buy three $5\frac{1}{2}$p stamps (those were the days!) for my entries for the Brain-teaser, Crossword and Mephisto; but finding a long queue there I bought a 10p book of stamps from a machine, which contained two stamps at each of the following denominations: 2p, $1\frac{1}{2}$p, 1p, $\frac{1}{2}$p. Since I already had four stamps of total value $6\frac{1}{2}$p left over from a similar 10p book I now had just enough stamps for the three entries.

I stuck four of the stamps totalling $5\frac{1}{2}$p on my Brain-teaser entry, but then found that there was room for only three stamps on the Crossword entry (because entrants have to write 'Crossword' on the top left-hand corner of the envelope) and the stamps I had left could not be arranged to give me three stamps totalling $5\frac{1}{2}$p for the Crossword entry and five for the Mephisto entry.

What were the denominations of the stamps on the Brain-teaser entry **?**

It is natural enough to set one's puzzles in an imaginary land to avoid the risk of inflation or decimalisation making them out-of-date. Here are two such inflation-proofed examples.

12 | *The Deflating Mangoes*

The Lotaseetas have a rather casual attitude to commerce. Every Monday morning, Ming, the rice-planter, gathers from the grove outside his bungalow a number of mangoes of uniform weight. For the rest of the week he uses these as weights for measuring out the rice on his scales, charging each customer according to the number of mangoes required to balance the weight purchased.

Unfortunately, the mangoes themselves lose a fixed percentage of their weight each day by evaporation. However, Ming roughly compensates for this by using two mangoes as the unit on Wednesdays and Thursdays and three on Fridays. Clearly, Wednesday is a good day for buying rice and Tuesday is a bad day.

His first customer at precisely 10 o'clock each morning (they are late risers) is Fung, the rice merchant, who always buys the same quantity of rice for his shop. On Monday Fung's rice cost him 243 cowries. On Friday it cost him 256 cowries.

How much did it cost him on Tuesday **?**

We were visiting the island state of Kimbu and had come to the post-office to send off some parcels to friends at home. The island's currency is the pim, and the postmaster told us that he had only stamps of five different face-values, as these had to be used up before a new issue of stamps was introduced.

These stamps were black, red, green, violet and yellow, in descending order of values, the black being the highest denomination and the yellow the lowest.

One parcel required stamps to the value of 100 pims and we were handed 9 stamps, 5 black, one green and 3 violet. The other two parcels required 50 pims' worth each, and for these we were given two different sets of 9 stamps.

One consisted of 1 black and 2 of each of the other colours, and the other set contained 5 green and 1 of each of the others.

What would have been the smallest number of stamps needed for a 50-pim parcel, and of which colours **?**

Posts of a different sort form a popular theme for Brain-teasers, with such openings as 'Mr Smith, Mr Brown and Mr Underwood were, not necessarily respectively, a metal-worker, a sun-tan lotion manufacturer, and a funeral director . . .' Our four examples of redeployment are a little less clichéd.

14 | *First-Class Post*

On Trafalgar Day each of the five Sea Lords will take over a post now occupied by one of the others. Each predicts what will happen; those whose predictions are right will get more senior posts, and those whose predictions are wrong will get more junior posts.

The most junior speaks first:

Fifth Sea Lord – Two Sea Lords will make a direct exchange.
Fourth Sea Lord – The Third Sea Lord will become the Second Sea Lord.
Third Sea Lord – A man who makes a true prediction will take over my job.

Of the First and Second Sea Lords each predicts the same future new post for himself.

Which post is that ?

Ashley, Bill, Charles, David and Edward are (not necessarily in that order) a dustman, a grocer, a miner, a blacksmith, and an artist, and all live on the right-hand side of Strife Lane, in even numbered houses. All five are of different ages and no man has reached the age of retirement (65). All of course are upright and honest citizens, and never tell lies. However, I had forgotten what job each man did, where he lived and how old he was, and so, to help me, each man volunteered the following statements:

Ashley: (1) The artist lives at No. 10, next to Charles;
          (2) Nobody lives next to the grocer although Bill is only two doors away;

Bill: (3) I am the only man whose age is indivisible by 9;
          (4) I am 4 years older than Ashley;

Charles: (5) The blacksmith's age is 5 times his house number;

David: (6) The miner lives 4 houses higher up the road from me;
          (7) The miner's age is 3 times the dustman's house number but he is two-thirds the dustman's age;

Edward: (8) The dustman is twice as old as David;
          (9) I am the oldest man in the street.

At which number does Ashley live
How old is the grocer
Who is the artist

?

Professor Knowall has recently become very interested in dreams.

A friend of mine has been doing some research about the extent to which dreams can be used to foretell the future. He persuaded his five employees (Alf, Bert, Charlie, Duggie and Ernie) to help him in his inquiries. They liked the idea of being in the forefront of anything new and their beds seemed a nice cosy place for research.

They met a year ago, and predicted their jobs now. Thus:

  (i)   *Alf:*   Ernie will not be the Door-Opener.
 (ii) *Bert:*   Duggie will not be the Bottle-Washer.
(iii) *Charlie:*   Alf will not be the Welfare Officer.
(iv) *Duggie:*   Ernie will be the Bottle-Washer.
 (v) *Ernie:*   Bert's prediction will be true.

Their jobs now are those of Bottle-Washer, Welfare Officer, Door-Shutter, Door-Opener and Worker.

The Professor was most interested in this.

'But, my dear Sergeant Bungle,' he said, 'how many of these predictions were correct and who made them?'

In fact only two of the predictions were correct and they were made by the men who became the Welfare Officer and the Worker.

What are all their jobs now   **?**

17 | *When Rules Were Rules*

No organisation can be efficient without clear-cut rules setting out exactly the rewards and the responsibilities of those who have the honour to be members of the team.

I came across the other day a copy of the rules which, as the Managing Director of Our Factory, I had put on the Society's Notice Board for all to see and understand. But this was many years ago when the pound was worth something, and when Rules were obeyed.

There were five employees in the Factory then, and their names were Alf, Bert, Charlie, Duggie and Ernie. Their jobs, not necessarily respectively, were those of Door-Opener, Door-Shutter, Door-Knob-Polisher, Bottle-Washer and Welfare Officer. The notice which I put up read as follows:

RULES

1 Charlie is to get 10% more than the worst paid of you all.
2 Alf is to be paid more than Duggie.
3 The Bottle-Washer is to get 5% more than 10% less than Bert.
4 Duggie is to get either £1 more or £1 less than Ernie.
5 The Door-Opener's wages are to be an odd multiple of 10p.
6 Ernie is to get 20% more than £1 less than the Door-Knob-Polisher.
7 The Door-Shutter is to be the best paid of you all.
8 Your wages are all to be different and each one is to be a multiple of 10p.
9 No one is to get more than £20 or less than £10 per week.

What are their weekly wages **?**

Do you detect a social comment in that last teaser, both in the title and in the list of jobs? Of course, puzzlers are not beyond a social comment or two; indeed, they often suggest ways of improving the system, as we've already seen in 'Stamp Expert'. Here are some more examples where writers have suggested improvements to our established procedures. The coffee and tea machine puzzle is included in this batch because we feel that *any* change would be an improvement.

18 | *Pow! Wham!*

The State of Inertia, in a last-ditch effort to revive an ailing economy, has decided to go ahead with the controversial innovation of adding two new digits

> POW! (Written ↑)
> WHAM! (Written ↓)

thus symbolising the stark alternatives facing the nation.

In a massive referendum on the relative merits, the country came down in favour of POW! carrying the greater weight and accordingly WHAM! is interposed in a lower position than POW! among the ten old digits, the usual order of which is retained.

Teething troubles from the consequential change to duodecimal-based arithmetic and to the new values of some of the old digits, are minimised by the free provision to everyone of school-age or over of PEST, an appropriate Pocket Electronic Summary Tabulator.

To enable a check to be made on the correct working of the instruments every PEST comes with the answers to 35×64 and 54×66, one consisting entirely of the new shapes and the other of neither of them.

What are the two answers ?

19	*An Efficient Type*

My typewriter had the standard keyboard:.

row 1: QWERTYUIOP
row 2: ASDFGHJKL
row 3: ZXCVBNM

until I was persuaded by a time-and-motion expert to have it 'improved'. When it came back I found that none of the letters was in its original row, though the numbers of letters per row remained unchanged. The expert assured me that, once I got used to the new system, it would save hours.

I tested it on various words connected with my occupation – I am a licensed victualler – with the following results. The figures in parentheses indicate how many rows I had to use to produce the word.

BEER	(1)	STOUT	(1)
SHERRY	(2)	WHISKY	(3)
HOCK	(2)	LAGER	(2)
VODKA	(2)	CAMPARI	(2)
CIDER	(3)	FLAGON	(2)
SQUASH	(2, but would have been 1 but for a single letter)		

Despite feeling a trifle MUZZY (a word which I was able to type using two rows) I persevered, next essaying CHAMBERTIN.

Which rows, in order, did I use   **?**

Recently a hot-drink vending machine was installed in our office. Very nice it is too – completely up to date it was when it was bought. There are five switches, a slot for your money, and a button. The switches are labelled TEA, COFFEE, CHOCOLATE, MILK and SUGAR, and you select the combination you want, put in your money, press the button, and out comes your drink. Why, you can even have coffolatea if you want!

At least, this is the idea. Unfortunately, during the ten years it has been in store, 'awaiting approval', mice have chewed up the wiring. Mice with soldering irons, I should think. The result is now that no switch affects its 'own' ingredient at all, but instead turns on two other ingredients, each ingredient being turned on by two different switches. However, if two switches are set which turn on the same ingredient, then they cancel each other out, and that ingredient doesn't come out at all.

The result is somewhat chaotic, though occasionally some of the output is actually drinkable. For instance, when you ask for white sweet coffee, you get unsweetened milky tea; when you ask for sweet milky chocolate, you get sweet chocolate without milk; and when you ask for unsweetened milky tea you get a glorious gooey mocha – i.e. chocolate and coffee with milk and sugar.

Luckily, pressing the 'deliver' button reinstates the original chaos, so that setting the same switches always gives the same results.

So, what is the easiest way to get white coffee without sugar
i.e. Name the fewest switches that will deliver just coffee and milk

We've grown tired of these low-scoring, defensive football matches in our locality, and so it was agreed last March for the annual competition between the five villages, each playing the others once, that no goalkeepers would be allowed, and each game would continue until nine goals had been scored.

Each village won 2 matches, and scored a different number of goals in each match. In the games, each possible result occurred twice. We had to decide the tournament on the total of goals scored, and happily, all five totals were different.

Blackton, the eventual champions, lost 2–7 to Appleton. Easton were last with 11 goals fewer than Blackton.

The Drafton centre-forward remarkably scored a hat-trick in each match, which included a last-second winner against Blackton.

Caxton scored in every match and could indeed have won the league if they had scored twice more in their match against Blackton. As it was they finished one goal ahead of Drafton in the final totals.

What was the score between Easton and Appleton; and what was the score between Caxton and Drafton ?

Puzzles about football are regular favourites. Despite the apparent restrictions of the football league tables, they can in fact provide a wide range of delightful logical teasers. Here are four excellent examples of the genre.

In this puzzle four football teams are going to play each other once during the course of the season. The incomplete table below shows the situation when some of the matches have been played (2 points for a win, 1 for a draw as usual).

The digits have been replaced by letters and each letter stands for the same digit wherever it appears and different letters stand for different digits.

The table looks like this

	Played	Won	Lost	Drawn	Goals		Points
					For	Against	
A	x			k	h	p	
B		h			m	m	
C	p	x	h	k	t		m
D	k						

List the matches played and the score in each match **?**

The doctors in the country town of Keepwell are keen soccer fans and with the assistance of their staff they have formed themselves into 3 teams who are all to play each other once.

I asked my friend, Dr Bungle, who is secretary of one of the teams, if he could let me know the current situation and he produced the following table:

	Played	Won	Lost	Drawn	Goals	
					For	Against
A	1	0	1	0	2	0
B	2	2	0	0	1	2
C	1	0	2	1	0	3

I knew that not more than 3 goals had been scored in any match and it did not take me long to see that there was something wrong with the table. I discovered subsequently that the doctor had been taking a non-truth drug of his own prescription. The drug was not 100% effective and so all but one of the figures were incorrect, and the remaining figure was correct.

What were the scores in the matches played so far ?

24 | *That's Torn It...*

It was typical of Uncle Bungle that he should have torn up the sheet of paper which gave particulars of the numbers of matches played, won, lost, drawn, etc of four local football teams who were eventually going to play each other once. The only piece left was as shown (as usual there are 2 points for a win and 1 for a draw).

Goals Against	Points
5	3
6	5
0	0
7	

It will not surprise those who know my Uncle to hear that one of the figures was wrong, but fortunately it was only one out (i.e. one more or less than the correct figure).

Each side had played at least one game, and not more than seven goals were scored in any match.

Calling the teams A, B, C and D in that order, find the score in each match ?

Last time it was vertical. But no one could accuse Uncle Bungle of being consistent and this time it was horizontal. The way, I mean, in which he tore the piece of paper on which were written the details of the matches between 4 local football teams, A, B, C and D, who are to play each other once.

All that was left was:

	Played	Won	Lost	Drawn	Goals For	Against
A	3	1	0	2	7	5
B	3	2	1	0	5	5

It is not known whether all the matches have been played. Not more than 7 goals were scored in any game.

With the information that it is possible to discover the score in each match you should be able to discover it.

What was the score in each match ?

We now have a complete change of theme. The next four teasers have all been touched by the long arm of the law, and, apart from that point in common, they provide as varied a bunch of twisters as you could wish to meet.

26 | *The Seven Criminals*

The instructor at the police training college spoke to the six constables in his class in these words:

'You have been studying full-face photographs of seven criminals whom we are calling P, Q, R, S, T, U and V. Now I am going to show you one photograph, taken in profile, of each criminal, and you have to write down their names in the order in which I present them.'

This was done and the constables handed in the following six answers:

```
1   P   Q   R   S   T   U   V
2   P   Q   R   U   T   S   V
3   P   S   U   V   R   T   Q
4   P   S   Q   U   R   T   V
5   P   U   R   V   T   S   Q
6   R   P   U   Q   T   S   V
```

'I am pleased to see that each criminal has been correctly identified by at least one of you,' said the instructor. 'I note that you all have a different number of correct answers and so I can give out the prizes.'

In what order were the photographs presented ?

'You see, Inspector, the combination of my safe is a six-figure number. In case anyone needed to get into it while I was away, I gave each of my clerks (Atkins, Browning and Clark) one of the two-figure numbers which make up the combination. I also told each the position in the combination of the number of another clerk, but not the number itself.

'Browning must have overheard me telling a friend that it is a coincidence that two of these numbers are squares and if you put them together you get a four-figure number that equals the other clerk's number squared. I remember I also said something about whether or not the combination is divisible by this clerk's number.

'When he was caught, Browning said, "I can't understand why the alarm went off; I know Clark's is the first number." I later realised that what I'd told my friend about whether or not that other number was a factor was wrong, which was lucky for me as Browning had got his own number in the right place.'

What was the combination **?**

It was a frightened, breathless, but very charming young lady who knocked on my office door late one night.

'They have gone,' she said: 'the Rajah's rubies are no longer in their ancestral home.'

I visited the scene of the crime and discovered a tattered piece of paper on which was written

$$
\begin{array}{r}
\underline{\quad O\ -\ S\ U} \\
N\,U\,)\underline{-\ D\ E\ E\ F\ -} \\
\underline{N\ U} \\
U\ R\ - \\
\underline{D\ T\ E} \\
\ S\ H\ - \\
\underline{\ U\ T\ =} \\
\ D\ F\ D \\
\underline{\ D\ T\ -} \\
\ \underline{\underline{T}} \\
\end{array}
$$

4936270681427669705719691270187069477266.

Some years ago I was lecturing to a group of policemen and I set them a traffic problem which they found difficult. Here it is:

A column of vehicles 10 miles long drives 24 miles at a constant speed and then halts. A policeman on a motor-cycle starts at the back of the column as it moves off, he rides to the front, turns round immediately and rides to the back of the column arriving at the moment the vehicles halt.

Assuming that his speed has been constant throughout:

How far has he ridden ?

Our law-breaking variations are not restricted to mundane police duties like jewel thefts and traffic patrols. We now delve into the world of espionage, without which no contemporary paperback would be complete.

30 | *Fiendish Device*

'Moriarty speaking,' said the voice on the telephone to the Prime Minister. 'As you have rejected my demands a hidden bomb will destroy London. I'm particularly pleased with the detonating device,' he went on, chuckling fiendishly, 'it's designed to give me time to get away before the explosion. There are 60 switches (all turned OFF at the moment) arranged in a ring so that No. 60 is next to No. 1. Whenever any switch changes from ON to OFF it causes the following switch to change over virtually instantaneously (from OFF to ON or vice-versa). As soon as I put down this phone I'll activate the device. This will automatically put switch No. 1 to ON, then one minute later to OFF, then one minute later still to ON, carrying on in this way after each minute changing switch No. 1 over. As soon as every switch has remained in the OFF position for 10 seconds simultaneously the bomb explodes. So goodbye now – for ever!'

The Prime Minister turned anxiously to Professor D. Fuse who had been listening in. 'When will the activating device set off the bomb?' he asked.

What was the Professor's reply ?

To code his message, the Agent began by writing three words – each word being a number, e.g. FIVE. In doing this, he did not write any single letter of the alphabet more than once.

For each of the letters thus written, he then substituted a digit and, in doing so, he used each of the digits 0 to 9 inclusive once (and once only).

He now had three numbers (all in figures) each of which was a perfect square. By adding these three numbers together, he obtained a total running to five figures.

In place of the digits in this total he now wrote the letters for which each of them had originally been substituted. This gave the letters NONSO.

What were the three perfect squares – in figures **?**

Seating your guests for a meal, it seems, is more difficult than the actual cooking. For those whose culinary skills go beyond scrambling eggs, here are some puzzles of the *unscrambling* variety.

Engagement Party

Alf Walker and Jill Jones celebrated their engagement at a dinner party with younger members of their families and some friends. Of the men, two were named Smith, two Jones, and two Walker; these were similarly the maiden names of the women.

The party of six couples sat at a rectangular table, one pair at each end, and two pairs along each side. Engaged and married couples, also men and women, were arranged alternately around the table. Nobody was engaged or married to, or sat opposite to, anyone of the same original surname.

Alf, with Jill on his left, sat at the table head, and Don and Greta sat at the foot. Two sisters, Ivy and Lena, were on Alf's side of the table, while Jill's brother Eddy sat next to Jill on her side. Fred and Lena each sat between a Smith and a Jones.

Others present were Jill's school friend Kate, Alf's friend Bill and his sister Hilda, and Cyril and his sister Greta.

Name the other engaged couples **?**

Brainbenders and Co., the noted games and puzzles manufacturers, held their office party recently.

The eight from the planning department shared one round table. Pat Robinson and Ann arrived together. Miss Davis looked sensational in her new dress and Mr Armstrong's suit was fresh from the cleaners.

Red-haired John sat on Miss Jones's right while Mary sat next-but-one to both Miss Brown and Miss Stevens.

Joan only had eyes for Mr Evans, opposite her, while her neighbour, Edna, was interested in Fred, who was sitting beside Bill and next-but-one to Miss Stevens.

Mr Smith was the only man between two girls and Miss Brown the only girl between two fellows. However, only two people sat opposite a person of their own sex.

What was the seating plan **?**

34 | *Prescription Description*

'We have just been discussing our health,' said Alf, 'and we have discovered that between us we share the same five complaints, and the same prescribed tablets for them. Each of us has two complaints, but no two have both the same, and no more than two of us take each sort of tablets. For instance two take red tablets, two blue, and so on. I do not have green ones. I take one lot the same as Ed, but they are not yellow, and I do not take kidney tablets.'

Bob said 'I do not have green tablets. One heart patient also has tablets for sleeplessness.'

Cyril said 'I do not have kidney tablets. I take one lot the same as Ed which are not for the heart. I do not take blue ones.'

Don said 'I do not have heart trouble. My tablets are not yellow. Those who take green tablets do not also take blue ones.'

Ed said 'I take white tablets which are not for the heart. The ones with nerves do not have indigestion, and nerve tablets are not yellow.'

What colour were the heart tablets
Who took those for nerves **?**

35 | *Moving NEWS*

Four friends and I live in the same town, one of us at the Town
Centre, and others at places due North, South, East and West
of the Town Centre. Our names are North, South, East, West
and Middle, but we do not necessarily live at the places which
accord with our names.

In visiting one another we use the only connecting roads
which run north–south and east–west through the Town
Centre.

Before last year, when North and I exchanged houses (to
accommodate his increasing family, mine by then having left
home), I lived farther North than West, who lives farther East
than Middle, who lives farther West than East. North lived
farther East than South. (When visiting East, North had to
turn right at the Town Centre, but I could go straight ahead
when visiting North.)

What is my name, and who lives in the
North, East, South, West and Middle
positions respectively **?**

36 | *A Cake Mix*

A small party was held to promote a brand of Cake Mix. There were five varieties of cake, five beverages, and five sorts of savouries offered.

I asked a sample group of five what they had chosen, and learned that each had had a different drink, a different slice of cake and two savouries.

No one had picked the same two savouries as any other, and no more than two people had the same savoury.

No one had cake of the same flavour as her beverage (tea being paired with plain sponge in this case).

Dot told me that she had no coffee in any form, no cheese and no egg, but she did have a sausage roll and one thing with orange flavour.

Eve had lemon drink, but no egg, and said that the one who had both egg and cheese did not drink coffee, but the tea drinker had cheese nibbles.

Fran said the one who drank chocolate had lemon cake. Fran had shrimp vol-au-vent, and only one of the shrimp eaters had lemon in either form.

Gill had a sausage roll and one orange item, and said that the one who had cheese had chocolate cake.

Helen told me that the one who had coffee cake had a ham sandwich, but no cheese, and no one had stuffed egg as well as shrimp.

Who had the ham sandwiches ?

Having had some 'round the table' teasers, we continue our teasers in the round by going round the garden and round the pond. These circular exercises offer pleasant pieces of applied geometry to illustrate to doubters that geometry is not dead.

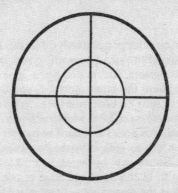

Our garden has paths as shown in the plan above. At each junction of paths there is a different variety of plant. The shortest walk (along the paths) from the Marigold to the Sneezewort passes only the Tickseed, and the shortest walk from the Nasturtium to the Quitch passes two plants, one of which is the Lobelia.

My wife suffers from hay fever and so she never walks past the irritating Rosemary, Sneezewort or Tickseed. We are still able to walk together on the shortest route from the Polyanthus to the Nasturtium (past one other plant), but she has to walk over twice as far as I in going from the Orpine to the Marigold.

List the plants, in order, which my wife passes when taking her shortest route from the Nasturtium to the Marigold

38 | Round the Pond

In our park is a circular pond exactly 50 metres in diameter, which affords delight to small boys who go down with ships.

Two such youngsters, Arthur and Boris, took their model motor-cruisers there the other morning, and decided on a race. Each was to start his boat from the extreme North of the pond at the same moment, after which each was to run round the pond to await his boat's arrival. The moment it touched shore its owner was to grab it by the bows and run with it directly to the South gate of the park, situated exactly 27 metres due South of the Southern edge of the pond. Both boats travelled at the same speed (1 metre in 3 seconds) but both owners, burdened with their respective craft, could manage only 3 metres in 4 seconds over the rough grass.

When the race started, Arthur's boat headed due South, but that of Boris headed somewhat East of South and eventually touched shore after travelling 40 metres in a straight line.

Who arrived first at the gate, and by what time margin (to the nearest second) ?

39 | *In the Pond*

The goldfish and the shubunkin swim in straight lines and at the same speed, and they always make right-angled turns when they do turn.

From a point on the edge of the Round Lake (a perfect circle, of course) the goldfish swam due north and the shubunkin swam in a direction somewhere between north and east.

After an hour the goldfish reached the edge of the lake and turned right; simultaneously the shubunkin turned right.

Half an hour later the shubunkin reached the edge of the lake, and 15 minutes after that the goldfish again reached a point on the edge of the lake.

The shubunkin, having rested for 15 minutes, wants the longest possible swim now without reaching a point on the edge of the lake.

What course should the fish steer **?**

The next two puzzles seem totally unrelated to the world of geometry, but in both cases the authors have chosen to give solutions from 'graph theory', a modern branch of geometry.

My wife and I attended a formal dinner at which there were just eight other people, namely the four couples Mr and Mrs Ailsa, Mr and Mrs Blackler, Mr and Mrs Caroline and Mr and Mrs Duncan. Introductions were made, and a certain number of handshakes took place (but, of course, no one shook hands with him/herself, nor with his/her spouse, nor more than once with anyone else). At the end of the evening I asked each other person how many hands they had shaken, and I was surprised to find that all the answers given were different. Also, the total of the number of handshakes made by the other four men was the same as the total of handshakes made by all five women.

The only woman I shook hands with was my old friend Mrs Ailsa. We had a long chat and then I took her to one side and, being a jealous fellow, I asked her whose hands my wife had shaken. She was unable to tell me, but luckily I was able to work it out later from the above information.

Whose hands did my wife shake
How many hands did Mrs Ailsa shake ?

The artist Pussicatto was exhibiting his new painting. It consisted of a 5-by-5 square of small squares with some of the small squares coloured black and the rest of the small squares coloured white.

The forger Coppicatto sent six of his assistants to make copies of different parts of the painting. They returned with

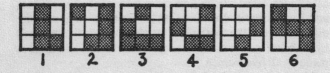

1   2   3   4   5   6

Unfortunately five of the assistants could not remember which way up their parts should go, and the other assistant, who gave his part the right way up, had copied the colour of one of the small squares wrongly. However the other five parts did cover the whole of the original painting.

Reproduce the original Pussicatto painting **?**

We move from circles to squares. There are many readers who find the following type of problem sheer magic. These puzzles consist of finding square arrays of numbers whose rows, columns, and diagonals have the same sum. Here for your perusal, then, are three Magic Squares.

42 | *A Magic Class*

The class only had nine pupils.

Three girls sat in the front row, three boys in the back one, while in the middle rows the sexes sat alternately.

Altogether, including the teacher, the sexes were equally divided.

When their home-work was returned marks were compared and the children were surprised to discover that the total marks gained by those in each row were the same, as were also those for each column from front to back and for each diagonal of the square in which they sat.

Excitedly they pointed out that fact to the teacher who replied that, when checking their work, which had been marked out of ten, he noticed that every digit had been used once and once only.

Three was the lowest mark awarded to a girl.

What was the highest mark given to a boy ?

43 Another Magic Class

This puzzle concerns a class of twenty-five pupils whose first names happen to have different initials (and none begins with X). The teacher makes them sit in alphabetical order in five neat rows of five with Arthur sitting to the left of Barry and in front of Freda.

When their homework was returned (marked, as usual, out of a maximum of 25 without using fractional marks) they found that each pupil had a different mark and that, surprisingly enough, the total of marks in each row of five, each column of five and each diagonal of five was identical.

Yvonne came top, followed by Harry and Jane in that order. Ursula scored more marks than Zena, and Richard was beaten by Charles. Victor had twice as many marks as George, and Ivor had four times as many as Freda. Susan beat Michael by the same margin by which Michael beat George (who, incidentally, scored an odd number of marks). This was also the margin by which Walter beat his left-hand neighbour and by which his right-hand neighbour beat him.

Kenneth beat Olga.
By how many marks **?**

'Here,' said Uncle Henry to the twins, 'is a magic square which I've started for you.'

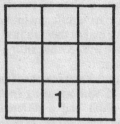

'You must complete it by putting 8 different *prime* numbers in the eight empty squares, so that the lines, the columns and the diagonals add up to the same total; and it must be the smallest possible total under the conditions.' There followed half an hour of comparative peace . . . after which the twins could bear it no longer. 'Oh, Uncle,' complained Betty, 'it looks so easy and yet it's *much* too difficult.' And Brian fervently agreed.

'All right,' said Uncle Henry, 'I'll tell you a couple more things: the number in the middle square is the average of the two numbers directly above and directly below it; the third largest number is NOT in the right-hand column, and every square contains one or two digits.'

After about a further ten minutes the twins managed to produce the right solution.

Can you   **?**

The son of a colleague has recently been working out 'triangular numbers', i.e. numbers which are the sum of consecutive integers from 1 upwards. So, for example, 1, 3, 6 and 10 are all triangular numbers. The little lad was asked by his father to work out the smallest triangular number over 100, and after some calculations he gave the correct answer of 105. Then he was asked for the smallest triangular number over 200, and the boy immediately guessed at 210. 'No', said his father, 'triangular numbers don't work like that.' So the son painstakingly found the smallest triangular number over 200 and found, by chance, that it *was* 210! No doubt this idea will at some time appear as a Brain-teaser, for some of the best puzzles are based on odd properties of numbers observed by *Sunday Times*' readers. Here are three excellent examples.

45 | *Powerless*

I have here two positive single figure numbers each less than 9. Neither is a factor of the other. I add the larger number to the smaller.

Then, to that total I again add the original larger number, and to the new total I again add the original larger number and may if I like continue this process indefinitely, but never shall I obtain a total which is a 'power' of any whole number whatsoever.

What are the two numbers ?

On a recent bus journey I purchased the tickets for my wife and myself. On each was a four-figure number, and the sum of all eight digits was twenty-five. I remarked upon this to my wife who thereupon asked if any digit appeared more than twice in the total and whether the sum of the digits on either ticket was equal to thirteen. I answered both questions and my wife was able to deduce the two numbers on the tickets.

What were they ?

47 | *Christmas Shopping*

My three nieces Anne, Betty and Carole came to stay with me just before Christmas. When they arrived they handed over their 'present' money and as I wrote down the amounts (in pence) I noticed that they were 3-digit numbers using all nine digits (zero excluded) and that Anne had more than Betty and Carole had as much as the other two together.

I drove the girls into town to shop and as they entered the car to return home they again asked me to look after their money. As I jotted down the three amounts I noticed that they were 3-digit numbers using all nine digits as before.

Before I drove off they wanted to know how much each had spent. As I told them these amounts I was struck by the fact that they were 3-digit numbers again using all nine digits. I also added that Carole had spent exactly three-fifths of her money while Anne had spent a little more than three-fifths of hers.

How much did the three girls have for the rest of their stay ❓

By now you will have seen the huge variety of puzzles which appear in the Brain-teaser column. This is because of the similarly-huge variety of people who set them, ranging from the prolific authors to the readers who send in just one brilliant idea. So we dedicate this volume's final trio of puzzles, each unique in its own way, to those authors, far and wide.

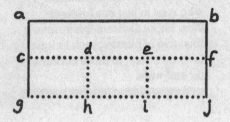

Our local pet shop caters especially for people who wish to keep mice in pairs. The shop sells three designs of half-cages and each customer buys two half-cages and joins them together to make a cage for two mice.

Each of the three designs of half-cages, the Astoria, the Dorchester and the Hilton, is based on the plan above and has 3 walls *ga*, *ab*, *bj* together with walls at some of *cd*, *de*, *ef*, *gh*, *hi*, *ij*, *dh* and *ei*. Each customer buys two half-cages of different designs and joins them together such that point *g* of each coincides with point *j* of the other. A mouse is then placed in area *abfc* of each and allowed to run freely except where it is prevented from going by the walls. There may be some parts of the overall cage which cannot be reached by either mouse.

The half-cages have been designed so that in no case can two mice reach each other and such that the following situation occurs: when an Astoria is joined to a Dorchester, the mouse from the Astoria has a larger area to move in than the other mouse; when a Dorchester is joined to a Hilton, the mouse from the Dorchester has a larger area; and when a Hilton is joined to an Astoria, the mouse from the Hilton has a larger area.

When I was last in the shop I noticed that the Astoria was the only cage with a wall at *dh*, and also that was the only cage with a wall at *ef*.

Draw a plan of the Dorchester and of the Hilton

49 | *Counting the Hours*

At school the other day, little Johnny was working with one of those boards with twelve clock-points regularly spaced round a circle against which should be put twelve counters showing the hours.

He was, in fact, in a bit of a daze about the whole thing and the only hour he was absolutely dead sure of was 12 whose counter he correctly placed. As for the eleven others, if the truth be told, he just put them around at random.

But Jill, his teacher, spotted some curious things. She first noticed that, however she chose a quartet of counters which formed the corners of a square, their sum was always the same.

Next, she saw that if she formed numbers by multiplying together the counters at the corners of each square, one of those numbers was more than six times one of the others.

She also observed that the counters in each quartet were, starting at the lowest, in ascending order of magnitude in the clockwise direction, and that 12 was not the only correct counter.

In break, she reported all this to her colleague, Mary, adding 'If I were to tell you, in addition, how many hours apart from the 12 Johnny had got right, you could tell me which they were.'

Which were they ?

50 | *Ups and Downs*

An electrician living in a block of flats has played a joke on the tenants by rewiring the lift. The buttons numbered 0 to 9 in the lift should correspond to the ground floor, first floor, etc, but he has rewired them so that although (for his own convenience) the buttons for the ground floor and his own floor work correctly, no other button takes you to its correct floor. Indeed when you get in the lift on the ground floor and go up, three of the buttons take you twice as high as they should, and two buttons take you only half as high as they should.

The milkman is unaware of the rewiring and so early yesterday morning, rather bleary-eyed, he followed his usual ritual which consists of taking nine pints of milk into the lift, pushing button 9, leaving one pint of milk when the lift stops, pushing button 8, leaving one pint of milk when the lift stops, and so on in decreasing order until, having pushed button 1 and having left his last pint, he usually returns to his van. However, yesterday when he tried to follow this procedure all seemed to go well until, having pushed button 1, when the lift stopped he found a pint of milk already there. So he took the remaining pint back to his van, with the result that just one of the tenants (who lived on one of the floors below the electrician's) did not get the pint of milk she'd expected.

The surprising thing was that during the milkman's ups and downs yesterday he at no time travelled right past the floor which he thought at that time he was heading towards.

List the floors which received milk, in the order in which the milkman visited them

THE SOLUTIONS

1 | *Pity the Postman*

DAVIES:	1 2 4 6 (total 13)			
BARKERS:	1 2 4 OR	1 2 6 OR	1 4 6 OR	2 4 6
WEBBS & BRIDGES chosen from ... (with two each)	1 2 1 2 4 6 1	1 2 4 1 2 4 1	1 2 1 2 4 1 2	1 1 2 1 2 4 1

But in each case the Webbs' total plus the Bridges' total is less than the Barkers' plus the Davies'. So, as Davies' > Barkers' and Webbs' > Bridges', the clue about equal totals tells us that

> Davies' total + Bridges' = Barkers' total + Webbs'

i.e.   Davies' total — Barkers' = Webbs' total — Bridges'

We now consider the possible values of Webbs' – Bridges' in the different cases specified above:

BARKERS:	1 2 4 : total 7	1 2 6 total 9	1 4 6 total 11	2 4 6 total 12
WEBBS – BRIDGES	$(6 + 4) -$ $(2 + 1)$ or $(6 + 2) -$ $(2 + 1)$ or less i.e. NEVER 6	$(4 + 2) -$ $(2 + 1)$ or less i.e. NEVER 4	$(4 + 2) -$ $(2 + 1)$ or $(4 + 1) -$ $(2 + 1)$ or less	$(4 + 2) -$ $(2 + 1)$ or $(4 + 1) -$ $(2 + 1)$ i.e. NEVER 1

So the only place where Webbs' – Bridges' can coincide with Davies' – Barkers' is in bold type.

Barkers 1, 4, 6; Webbs 1, 4

	Up or Down	Last week	This week	Possibles	Products
A	D	1	a	9	9
B		2	b	5, 8	10
C	D	3	c	7	21
D	U	4	d	3	12
E		5	e	8, 10	40
F	U	6	f	2, 1	
G	U	7	g	6	42
H		8	h	10	80
I	U	9	i	4	36
J	U	10	j	8, 5, 2, 1	

This chart contains the information gradually gleaned from the deductions below.

(a) $7g = 6c$ so $c = 7$ and $g = 6$

(b) $9i = 12d$ so $i = 4$ and $d = 3$, or $i = 8$ and $d = 6$. But the latter is ruled out since $g = 6$

(c) The known U's D's are filled in and it follows that B, E, H are down

(d) Products B, D, E, F, G, H, I, J are even; and C is odd. So, as total is even, A's product is odd and $a = 9$ (to give it the biggest single drop). Fill in the remaining possibles as shown.

(e) $h = 10$ implies $e = 8$ and $b = 5$; eliminate these elsewhere, and fill in the products. So f is 2 or 1 and j is 1 or 2

(f) Total of products is $250 + 6.2 + 10.1 = 272$, or $250 + 6.1 + 10.2 = 276$

JFDIBGCEAH

The possible vote distribution for the five judges is:

```
0 1 2 3 9
0 1 2 4 8
0 1 2 5 7
0 1 3 4 7
0 1 3 5 6
0 2 3 4 6
1 2 3 4 5
```

Only one 5 is allowed and there are at most 4 zeros. So, 01257 and 01356 are invalid. Note: We require four of each number from 0 to 4, and one each from 5 to 9.

The girl with a 9 is at best 3rd. The girl who wins has a zero so the leading three scores can only be 84320 = 17, 64321 = 16 and 93210 = 15. The last two must total 14 and 13 and must have 7, 5, 4, 4, 3, 2, 1, 1, 0, 0 in their make up. So they are 7, 4, 2, 1, 0 and 5, 4, 3, 1, 0.

We can now put all the obvious information into a table:

		Judges					Marks still needed
	Votes	B		J		D	
GIRLS P R A	17	8					0,2,3,4.
	16	4	6				1,2,3.
	15	2		9			0,1,3.
	14	1			7		0,2,4.
	13	0				5	1,3,4.
still needed		0,2,3,4	0,1,2,3	0,1,3,4		1,2,3,4	

(1) B puts A last, so G does not win; hence L wins and G is 4th; and R gets 0 from the fourth column.

(2) Complete R's line.

(3) A's line must now read 0,4,1,3,5 with T being column two, and S column four.

(4) We can now complete G's line and J's column and the rest follows at once.

(5) Linda wins with marks B8, S4, D3, T2, J0.

 Linda wins with marks from Brian 8, Sam 4, Dan 3, Tom 2, Joe 0

4 | Synchronised Lights

1. Charlie travels the whole system in less than two minutes, so the total distance is less than 2½ miles, and no section is longer than 1¾ miles. We chart the three arrival times at all possible positions of the first light (green from 3–16 secs, 29–42 secs etc).

First light	Arrival time at 30 mph	Arrival time at 50 mph	Arrival time at 75 mph
⅛	15 secs	9 secs	6 secs
¼	30 secs	18 secs (RED)	
⅜	45 secs (RED)		
½	60 secs	36 secs	24 secs (RED)
⅝	75 secs (RED)		
¾	90 secs	54 secs (RED)	

And the only one allowing all three to pass is ⅛ mile.

2. Charlie arrives at the last light as it changes. A table of each ⅛ mile together with the light sequence times of traffic lights should they be situated there shows that the only distance where a light change coincides with Charlie's arrival is 1¼ miles after the start. (E.g. a light at ¼ mile after the start would have green showing 15 seconds later than at the first light; a light at ⅜ mile would have green showing 30 seconds later etc.)

3. The same chart as in 2 shows that, as Charlie is not stopped, there is no light at ¼, ⅝ or 1 mile from the start. The information about Bert enables the rest of the distances to be calculated.

     ⅛, ¼, ⅜, ⅛, ¼, ⅛

5 | *Ding-Dong*

Let there be N days between consecutive Feasts, with dongs every x minutes and dings every $x+p$ minutes (or vice-versa). The two noises alternate between Feasts and so the situation is

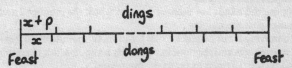

The pauses between successive noises are $p, 2p, 3p, \ldots, 3p, 2p, p$. Since one of these is one minute it follows that $p = 1$.
Now the first ding is 1 minute after the first dong;
the second ding is 2 minutes after the second dong;
the xth ding is x minutes after the xth dong,
    WHICH IS THE TIME OF ANOTHER DONG.
Therefore in the N days (= 1440.N minutes) between Feasts there are exactly x intervals of $x+1$ minutes; i.e. $x(x+1) = 1440.N$.

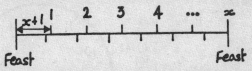

So the problem is to find a prime number N such that 1440.N is the product of two consecutive integers. The obvious candidates are N = 1439 and 1441 (= 11 × 131) and indeed 1439 *is* prime. The conscientious reader who wishes to show that 1439 is the *only* solution can factorise $1440.N = 2^5 \cdot 3^2 \cdot 5$. N into two groups (e.g. $2^5.3^2$ and $5.N$) and observe that they never differ by 1.

● **1439 days**

Let position of hands just after 2.20 be called '1st position', and just after 4.10 '2nd position'.

Suppose the hands are situated x minutes past the number 2 and y minutes past the number 4.

In moving from 2 o'clock to 1st position, the minute hand travels $20 + y$ minutes and the hour hand travels x minutes. But the minute hand travels 12 times as far as the hour hand,

Therefore,
$$20 + y = 12x \qquad (1)$$

Again, in moving from 4 o'clock to the 2nd position, the minute hand travels $10 + x$ minutes and the hour hand travels y minutes,

Therefore,
$$10 + x = 12y \qquad (2)$$

Multiplying equation (1) by 12 and substituting for $12y$ from equation (2),

$$240 + 10 + x = 144x$$
i.e.
$$250 = 143x$$
therefore
$$x = 250/143$$
$$= 1\frac{107}{143}$$

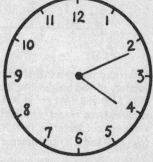

Now the time was $10 + x$ past 4

i.e. $11\frac{107}{143}$ minutes past 4

  $11\dfrac{107}{143}$ minutes past 4

It is evident from either the second or last sentences of the puzzle that the period of observation must be less than 8 days, and, since the two clocks are stated to be keeping different times and gaining or losing less than 60 minutes per day, it is clear that they cannot *both* be gaining or losing for the faster could not then 'lap' the slower (by 12 hours) in so short a period. Hence one of the clocks must be gaining say X minutes per day and the other losing say Y minutes per day. Thus after a true elapsed time of M minutes the two clocks will have

respectively moved forward $M \times \dfrac{1440 + X}{1440}$ and $M \times \dfrac{1440 - Y}{1440}$

minutes, and for both to show the same hour the difference between these two movements must equal 12 hours (720 mins.) or some multiple thereof,

i.e. $\dfrac{M(X + Y)}{1440} = 720$ etc.

or $M = \dfrac{720 \times 1440}{(X + Y)}$ etc.

And since M is known to be integral and less than 8×1440 minutes, $(X + Y)$ must be a factor of 720×1440 which exceeds 90 but is less than 120 (since X, Y are each less than 60).

The only such factors are 96, 100 and 108.

Now if $(X + Y)$ were 96, the true elapsed time M would be 10,800 minutes or 7 days plus 12 hours and would have terminated outside working hours with the coincidence of the clocks therefore unobserved. Similarly if $(X + Y)$ were 108, the true elapsed time would be 9,600 minutes or 6 days plus 16 hours which again would have terminated outside working hours (since 5 pm to 9.30 am is already 16½ hours).

continued overleaf

Thus (X + Y) can only be 100, giving a true elapsed time of 7.2 ×
1440 minutes or 7⅕ days, and since the clocks have moved forward
in total an exact number of minutes both X and Y must be multiples
of 5.

The alternatives, therefore, for the clock which is (say) gaining are
55, 50 or 45 minutes per day, corresponding with gains over the 7⅕
days of 6 hours 36 minutes, 6 hours, and 5 hours 24 minutes
respectively, and thus with total forward movements of (7 days plus)
11 hours 24 minutes, 10 hours 48 minutes and 10 hours 12 minutes
respectively. And since the clocks were showing a time of 8 o'clock,
the above correspond with original setting times of 8.36, 9.12 and
9.48, of which only 9.48 (the previous Monday morning) lies within
the working hours and is therefore the unique valid answer to the
puzzle.

(Note that the true time when the clocks showed 8 o'clock was 2.36
pm which is also within working hours.)

 Monday, 9.48 am

8 | *Old Father Prime*

Let a, b, c, d be the ages of Albert, Bert, Charlie and David respectively,

Then $$d+b=c \quad \text{and} \quad b+c=a=d^3$$

Re-writing $d + b = c$ as $d = c - b$ where b, c, d are prime, it is necessary to find two primes which differ by another prime. Most primes are odd and the difference between any two is even. There is only one even prime, i.e. 2.

Therefore $d = 2$ and $d^3 = a = 8$.

Thus Albert had his eighth anniversary in 1916 and was born in 1880 since 1916 was the eighth leap year after 1880 (1900 was not a leap year).

 1880

<table>
<tr><td></td><td colspan="2">9</td><td colspan="2">Prime
Birthdays</td></tr>
</table>

1. Since the numerical difference between the years of birth of Michael (M)'s father and mother respectively and that of any one of the others are *both* primes, those two years must differ by 2 – the only even prime.

2. The years of birth of M. and Noelle (N) – as also of the children – must therefore each exceed those of his parents by primes which likewise differ by 2, and the only such primes feasible for M and N are 19 (– 2 = 17) and/or 31 (– 2 = 29) and/or 43 (– 2 = 41).

3. But since M's mother was still in her twenties when her youngest was born, the only practicable primes for application to M are 19 or 31, and since the same was true of N the primes practicable for her/her youngest are 19/43 or 31/61 (– 2 = 59) or 43/73 (– 2 = 71).

4. Bearing in mind that, since twins, triplets, etc are precluded, only two children can have been born to N in any one year. The above options prove to offer only two feasible sets of primes which include one that is the mean of all the rest, thus:

	Father	Mother	Michael	Noelle	Children
I	—	2	31	31	61, 61
II	—	2	31	43	61, 61, 73, 73

But I is precluded since the mean of 31 is not 'unique' as stated but common to both M and N, so II only is valid and there are 4 children (born at opposite ends of two calendar years, 12 years apart).

5. The only possible pattern of years of birth is now established, the prototype and four succeeding examples of actual years being:

Father	1900	1901	1902	1903	**1904** etc etc
Mother	1902	1903	**1904**	1905	1906
Michael	1931	**1932**	1933	1934	1935
Noelle	1943	**1944**	1945	1946	1947
Children	1961	1962	1963	**1964**	1965
	1961 etc				
	1973 etc				
	1973 etc				

15544 ($\div$ 8 = 1943)

But each of the highlighted years is a leap year and as such precluded by the puzzle; moreover this quadrennial incidence clearly repeats over all ensuing years. Exceptionally, however, 1900 was *not* a leap year, and the only year in which Noelle can have been born is thus 1943 (around Christmas as her name suggests, so that she was 'still in her twenties' when her youngest arrived in late 1973).

⬤   **1943 and 4**

10 — *Stamp Expert*

Since $3 \times 6\frac{1}{2} = 19\frac{1}{2}$, one strip, and therefore every strip, must contain $\frac{1}{2}$.

Three strips must split either

    (a) $6\frac{1}{2}$, $8\frac{1}{2}$, $8\frac{1}{2}$, $6\frac{1}{2}$;   (b) $8\frac{1}{2}$, $6\frac{1}{2}$, $6\frac{1}{2}$, $8\frac{1}{2}$;

    (c) $6\frac{1}{2}$, $8\frac{1}{2}$, $6\frac{1}{2}$, $8\frac{1}{2}$;   (d) $6\frac{1}{2}$, $6\frac{1}{2}$, $8\frac{1}{2}$, $8\frac{1}{2}$;

    (or reflections).

(a)   (i)   Since the first strip starts $6\frac{1}{2}$, the third ends $6\frac{1}{2}$, and the second must split $5, 5$, and all strips are the same, each strip must have the form:

$$3\frac{1}{2} \quad 1\frac{1}{2} \quad 1\frac{1}{2} \quad 3\frac{1}{2}$$

    (ii)   Since no splitting of any of the above values x into $\frac{1}{2}$ and x-$\frac{1}{2}$ will give a $8\frac{1}{2}$ strip, (a) is impossible.

(b)   (i)   Following the argument of (a), each strip must have the form:

$$1\frac{1}{2} \quad 3\frac{1}{2} \quad 3\frac{1}{2} \quad 1\frac{1}{2}$$

    (ii)   The only way to introduce $\frac{1}{2}$ to allow $6\frac{1}{2}$ is $1\frac{1}{2}\,\frac{1}{2}\,3\,3\frac{1}{2}\,1\frac{1}{2}$, but two such joined strips cannot be split into $3 \times 6\frac{1}{2}$ plus $\frac{1}{2}$. Therefore (b) is impossible.

(c) and (d) each require a strip beginning $6\frac{1}{2}$ and ending $8\frac{1}{2}$, i.e.

$$1\frac{1}{2} \quad 5 \quad 3\frac{1}{2}$$

In splitting three 6½ blocks from two joined strips, there must be ½ which is wasted, either

(i) at the beginning,   i.e. ½ 1 5 ½ 3 : 3½ 6½
                           i.e. ½ 1 2 3 ½ 3 : ½ 1 2 3 ½ 3

(but this requires six stamps)

(ii) after the first 6½,   i.e. 1½ 5 ½ 3 : 3½ 6½
                          i.e. 1½ 2 3 ½ 3 : 1½ 2 3 ½ 3

(iii) after the second 6½, i.e. 1½ 5 3½ : 3 ½ 6½
                          i.e. 1½ 1½ ½ 3 3½ : 1½ 1½ ½ 3 3½

(iv) at the end   i.e. 1½ 5 3½ : 3 6½ ½
                          i.e. 1½ 1½ 3½ 3 ½ : 1½ 1½ 3½ 3 ½

However, three joined strips of type (ii) cannot be split into
2 × 6½ + 2 × 8½, whereas strips of types (iii) and (iv) can.

Type (iv) is preferred to allow the (final) spoiled stamp to be minimal (½p).

●   **1½p, 1½p, 3½p, 3p, ½p**

11 | *Those Were the Days*

If three stamps are to be used for the Crossword entry, they must be of denominations 2p, 2p, 1½p; so if it is impossible to use three stamps this must be because after the stamps have been used for the Brain-teaser entry *EITHER* (a) fewer than two 2p stamps remain *OR* (b) no 1½p stamps remain.

However, (a) is impossible: the incomplete book must contain two stamps at 2p (because without using two at 2p the greatest value that can be obtained from four stamps in a book is 2p + 1½p + 1½p + 1p = 6p); the complete book also contains two stamps at 2p, and since the Brain-teaser entry at 5½p cannot have used more than two stamps at 2p a total of at least two stamps at 2p still remain.

If (b) is to be true then (i) both 1½p stamps from the complete book must have been used for the Brain-teaser entry; (ii) since the incomplete book must have contained another 1½p stamp (because without using 1½p stamps the greatest value that can be obtained from four stamps in a book is 2p + 2p + 1p + 1p = 6p) this 1½p stamp must also have been used for the Brain-teaser entry.

Therefore three stamps at 1½p were used for the Brain-teaser entry, and the fourth stamp was at 1p. The remaining stamps are four at 2p, two at 1p and two at ½p.

 1½p, 1½p, 1½p, 1p

<table>
<tr><td>

12

</td><td>

The Deflating Mangoes

</td></tr>
</table>

Let the weight of one mango on Monday be W units, on Tuesday Wx, on Wednesday Wx^2, on Thursday Wx^3, and on Friday Wx^4. Then the cost of the quantity R of rice is

$$\text{Monday: } \frac{R}{W} \text{ currency units (243);}$$

$$\text{Tuesday: } \frac{R}{Wx} \text{ currency units;}$$

$$\text{Wednesday: } \frac{R}{2Wx^2} \text{ currency units;}$$

$$\text{Thursday: } \frac{R}{2Wx^3} \text{ currency units;}$$

$$\text{and Friday: } \frac{R}{3Wx^4} \text{ currency units (256).}$$

$$\therefore \quad \frac{\text{Monday}}{\text{Friday}} = 3x^4 = \frac{243}{256} \text{ and } x^4 = \frac{81}{256}$$

$$\therefore \quad x = \frac{3}{4} \text{ and Tuesday's cost is given by}$$

$$\text{Tuesday's cost} = \frac{\text{Monday's cost}}{x} = \frac{243}{\frac{3}{4}} = 324.$$

●   **324 cowries**

13 | *Overseas Mail*

The stamps are (by initials of colours): b, r, g, v and y, where $b > r > g > v > y$.

$$1b + 2r + 2g + 2v + 2y = 50 \quad \text{(A)}$$
$$1b + 1r + 5g + 1v + 1y = 50 \quad \text{(B)}$$
$$5b + 1g + 3v = 100 \quad \text{(C)}$$

From $2 \times$ (B) subtract (A) to give

$$b + 8g = 50$$

Since $g < b$ we must have

g	b	v
1	42	impossible
2	34	impossible
3	26	impossible
4	18	2
5	10	15

Hence, from (C), we can calculate v, as shown. Since $v < g$ it follows that

$$g = 4, \ b = 18, \ v = 2 \text{ (and hence } y = 1\text{), and (from (B)) } r = 9.$$

It is impossible to make up 50p with four or fewer stamps, and it is uniquely possible with five stamps.

 2 black, 1 red, 1 green and 1 yellow

1. As (5) must go to a more senior post, his prediction is right and there is a straight exchange (S E) between two Sea Lords.

2. If (4) becomes (5), then (3) does not become (2)

$$\left.\begin{array}{l}
\text{but } either \text{ (3) becomes (1)} \\
\therefore \text{ (5) becomes (3)} \\
or \text{ (3) becomes (4)} \\
\therefore \text{ (1) or (2) becomes (3)}
\end{array}\right\} \text{ No S E in either case.}$$

3. So (4) does not become (5)
Nor does (4) become (2) (as this makes (3) become (2) also)
If (4) becomes (1), (3) becomes (2), (5) becomes (3)
                         (1) becomes (4), and (2) becomes (5)
If (4) becomes (3), (3) becomes (2), (2) becomes (4)
                         (1) becomes (5) and (5) becomes (1)
Both these provide a S E and are therefore possible.

4. Now, as in both cases (1) and (2) become (4) and (5) and make the same (wrong) prediction, each must predict for himself the post of Third Sea Lord.

 Third Sea Lord

15 | *Job Allocation*

From (5) the blacksmith's age must be a multiple of 10, since the house numbers are even.

From (3) only Bill's age is indivisible by 9. Therefore Bill's age must be the multiple of 10. Therefore Bill must be the blacksmith.

From (4) Bill is 4 years older than Ashley. Therefore Ashley's age ends in 6. This can only be 36 (to be divisible by 9). Therefore Bill is 40.

From (5) Bill's house is no. 8.

From (7) the miner's age must be an even number divisible by 9, e.g. 18, 36, 54.

This makes the dustman 27, 54 or 81. 81 is impossible.

From (8) the dustman is twice as old as David, so David is either $13\frac{1}{2}$ or 27. He must be 27, so the dustman is 54, and the miner is 36 and must be Ashley.

From (9) Edward must be 63 (only number between 54 and 65 divisible by 9).

From (7) the dustman's house number is 36/3 = 12.

From (1) Charles must live at no. 12, i.e. he is the dustman.

From (2) the grocer must live at no. 4.

David is either the artist or the grocer, and must live at no. 4 or no. 10.

From (6) the miner lives at no. 12 or no. 18. He must live at no. 18.

Therefore David is the artist, and Edward is the grocer, being 63.

Ashley lives at 18
The grocer is 63
David is the artist

16 | *Job Prediction*

(1) *If (iv) true,* then E becomes B–W; ∴ (ii) true (if E is B–W, then D is not B–W); and (i) true (if E is B–W, then E is not D–O). But we are told that only two predictions are true. ∴ *(iv) cannot be true* ∴ E did not become B–W. (A diagram will help). Thus:

	B–W	W–O	D–S	D–O	Worker
A					
B					
C					
D					
E	X				

(The fact that E is not B–W has been put in. The reader is advised to put in other information on his own diagram).

(2) *Consider (v).* If true, then (ii) true, ∴ D not B–W. And all other predictions must be false (for only two predictions were true) ∴ (iii) must be false, ∴ A would be W–O. But we are told that W–O made one of the true predictions, ∴ our assumption is wrong, ∴ *(v) not true.* ∴ B's prediction not true, ∴ D becomes B–W.

(3) ∴ predictions (iv), (v) and (ii) are false.
∴ predictions (i) and (iii) are true.
∴ from (i) E not D–O, and from (iii) A not W–O.

continued overleaf

(4) A and C (who made correct predictions) are between them
W–O and Worker.
But we know that A did not become W–O, . . C became
W–O and A became Worker.

By elimination, B became D–O, and E became D–S.

**Alf became Worker
Bert became Door-Opener
Charlie became Welfare Officer
Duggie became Bottle-Washer
Ernie became Door-Shutter**

17 | *When Rules Were Rules*

We work in units of 10p, with all wages between 100 and 200 (inclusive).

(i)   From (3) BW gets $\frac{105}{100} \times \frac{90}{100} \times B = \frac{189}{200} \times B$. So BW earns 189 and B 200.

Also, B is the best paid and so is the DS.

(ii) From (6) E gets more than DKP. Hence E is not worst paid, E is $\frac{6}{5} \times (DKP - 10)$ and, being a multiple of 6, is not BW.

(iii) From (1), C's wage is $\frac{11}{10} \times$ worst wage, which cannot be 189.

Also, the worst wage must be a multiple of 10. So C is not BW: neither is C the worst paid, nor (by (2)) is A. So D is the worst paid.

(iv) From (5) DO cannot be D (a multiple of 10), nor E (a multiple of 6). So DO is C and, by elimination, D is DKP and E is WO.

(v)   E's wage is $\frac{6}{5} \times (D's - 10)$, which is a multiple of 12.

continued overleaf

(vi)   The possibilities are:

D	100	110	120	130	140	150	160	170
C	110	121	132	143	154	165	176	187
E	108	120	132	144	156	168	180	192

But from (4) D gets £1 more or £1 less than E.
So D must get 110, E gets 120, and C gets 121.

Alf (Bottle-Washer)   £18.90
Bert (Door-Shutter)   £20.00
Charlie (Door-Opener)   £12.10
Duggie (Knob-Polisher)   £11.00
Ernie (Welfare Officer)   £12.00

Consider where | and | are placed relative to 3, 4, 5 and 6. We give three typical cases:

0123 | *456* | *789*

Here '54 × 66' means 65 × 77 (duodecimal) or 77 × 91 (decimal) = 7007 (decimal) = $4.12^3 + 0.12^2 + 7.12 + 11$. So in the new symbols this would be | 069, which is not acceptable.

01234 | *5* | *6789*

Here '54 × 66' means 64 × 88 (duodecimal) or 76 × 104 (decimal) = 7904 (decimal) = $4.12^3 + 6.12^2 + 10.12 + 8$. So in the new symbols this would be 4586, which is acceptable.
But then '35 × 64' = 36 × 84 (duodecimal) = 42 × 100 (decimal) = 2520 (duodecimal) = 2 | 20 (new symbols) : unacceptable.

0123 | *45* | *6789*

Here '54 × 66' = 65 × 88 (duodecimal) = 77 × 104 (decimal)
= 8008 (decimal) = 4774 (duodecimal)
= | | | | :
and '35 × 64' = 36 × 85 (duodecimal) = 42 × 101 (decimal)
= 4242 (decimal) = 2556 (duodecimal)
= 2445 (new symbols)

| | | | and 2445

19 | An Efficient Type

	*Old Keyboard								New Keyboard								
Q	W	E	R	T	Y	U	I	O	P	Kd	Ce	Lf	Af	Gf	Vg	Fk	Nk	Xl	Jl
A	S	D	F	G	H	J	K	L		Ba	Ea	Ra	Ph	Ih	Wd/j	Yd/j	Zl	Ml
Z	X	C	V	B	N	M				Sb	Tb	Ob	Ub	Hc	Di	Qj

Notes: Asterisk * indicates OLD row-placing.
In NEW keyboard above, CAPITAL LETTERS indicate keyboard letters; lower case letters refer to clues below from which keyboard letters may be deduced step by step.

(a) BEER (1)
    *3 1 1 1   So, on new keyboard, all must be row 2.

(b) STOUT (1)
    *2 1 1 1 1   So, on new keyboard, all must be row 3.

(c)   SHERRY (2)
              *2 2 1 1 1 1
new   { 3 1 2 2 2 2   Rows must be 2/3, i.e. H in 3.
possibilities { 3   3

(d)   WHISKY (3)
              * 1 2 1 2 2 1
new   { 2 3 2 3 1 2   To give three rows, K is 1; at least one
possibilities { 3 3   3 3   W, I, Y is 2, and any not 2 are 3.

(e)   HOCK (2)
    new   3 3 ? 1   C must be 1 or 3, but 3 barred; so C is 1.

(f)   LAGER (2)
           *2 2 2 1 1
    new   { 1 1 1 2 2   L, A, G are ALL in 1 or ALL in 3. No room
           { 3 3 3   in 3; so all 1.

(g)   VODKA (2)
           *3 1 2 2 2
    new   { 1 3 1 1 1   Rows are 1/3; so V is 1.
           { 2 3

(h) CAMPARI (2)

new $\left\{\begin{array}{l} \text{*32 31 2 11} \\ \overline{\text{11 12 1 22}} \\ \quad \text{23} \quad \text{3} \end{array}\right.$ Rows must be 1/2; so P and I are 2.

(i) CIDER (3)

new 12?22 So D is 3.

(j) SQUASH (2) S, U, H are in 3; A is odd man out in 1. So Q *fills* row 3.

(k) FLAGON (2)

new $\left\{\begin{array}{l} \text{*222213} \\ \overline{\text{111131}} \\ \text{3} \quad\quad \text{2} \end{array}\right.$ F, N must be 1.

(l) MUZZY (2) U 3, Y 2 fixed. So M, Z in 2, leaving X, J for 1.

1312222321

C = Coffee, T = Tea, H = Chocolate, M = Milk, S = Sugar.
M —— ST means 'switching the milk switch turns on sugar and tea'.
H —+→ C means 'chocolate is not turned on by switching the coffee switch' etc.

Data: (a) $\left.\begin{array}{c}C\\M\\S\end{array}\right\}$ →MT   (b) $\left.\begin{array}{c}H\\M\\S\end{array}\right\}$ → SH   (c) $\left.\begin{array}{c}M\\T\end{array}\right\}$ →MSHC

In this cyclic situation, where the effect of switching on all the switches is to cancel them all out and produce a nil result, it can easily be shown that the effect of switching certain X switches is exactly the same as switching the remaining 5-X switches. So:

(d) $\left.\begin{array}{c}H\\T\end{array}\right\}$ →MT   (e) $\left.\begin{array}{c}C\\T\end{array}\right\}$ → SH   (f) $\left.\begin{array}{c}C\\H\\S\end{array}\right\}$ →MSHC

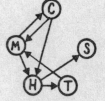

Data:

1 c Since M —+→ M, T —— M̄
2 d Since T —+→ T, H —— T
3 b Since H —+← H, M or S —— H
4 a Since M or S —— H, C removes H; i.e. C —— H.

5 f, b CHS — MSCH. MHS — S<u>H.</u> Therefore M, C are produced by addition from C — or by deletion by M — But C ←— C, M ←— M, so C — M, M — C.

6 f, a CSH — MSHC. CSM — MT. Therefore S, H, C, T are produced by addition from, or deletion by H, M — . We already have M — C, H — T, so, since H ←— H, then H — S, M — H.

7 With 7 of the 10 links established, the diagram can be completed unambiguously.

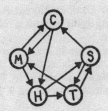

8 The completed diagram accounts for all the data, and is unique.

9 C ←— S or M; M — T or C. Try the 4 combinations: MC → CM, MM → CM as required. These 2 (and no other 2) switches work.

●   **Coffee and milk**

21 | *Shoot!*

The maximum score by any side is $9 + 8 + 4 + 3 = 24$
The minimum score by any side is $0 + 1 + 5 + 6 = 12$

Easton scored 11 less goals than Blackton, who lost one match 2–7, and so Easton scored a total of 12 (0, 1, 5, 6) and Blackton 23 (9, 8, 4, 2).

Caxton must have finished with 22, 21, or 20 goals, as 2 more goals in their match with Blackton would have made them champions. Examining these separately:

(a) Caxton 22 gives Drafton 21 and Appleton therefore 12, because the total goals scored is 90. But Appleton and Easton cannot tie.

(b) Caxton 21 gives Drafton 20 and Appleton 14. Appleton scored 7 in their match with Blackton, and therefore 7 in the other three matches, two of which they lost. From the Easton scores above, Appleton must have scored 9, 8, 4, or 3 against them, an impossibility.

(c) Caxton 20 gives Drafton 19 and Appleton 16, which is the solution.

Drafton with a minimum of 3 in each match, and 5 against Blackton will have scores of 3, 4, 5, and 7.

Blackton had losses against Appleton and Drafton, and therefore wins against Caxton and Easton. As Caxton scored in each match, Blackton must have got 8 against them. Allocation of the remaining scores gives Caxton getting 1, 2, 8 and 9, and Appleton 0, 3, 6, and 7. Thus the final table is easily constructed as:

	A	B	C	D	E
A	—	7	0	6	3
B	2	—	8	4	9
C	9	1	—	2	8
D	3	5	7	—	4
E	6	0	1	5	—

Easton 6, Appleton 3
Caxton 2, Drafton 7

Since the 4 teams are going to play each other once, no teams can have played more than 3 games.

In C's line the letters p, x, h and k must all be different and p must be bigger than the others.

$\therefore p = 3$, and x, h and k must be 0, 1 and 2, but we do not yet know which is which.

A and D played at least 1 match (for C played them all) $\therefore x$ and k cannot be 0, $\therefore h$ must be 0.

A played x and drew k, $\therefore x$ must be greater than k. $\therefore x = 2$ and $k = 1$. $\therefore$ C got 5 points (2 wins and a draw) $\therefore m = 5$.

Since the total of matches played must be even, B must have played 2.

D only played 1 game, $\therefore$ it was against C. And D v A and D v B were the only 2 matches that were not played.

B won none and had 5 goals for and 5 against. $\therefore$ they drew both their matches v A and v C.

A scored no goals but had 3 goals against. $\therefore$ A v B was 0–0, and A v C was 0–3.

Since B v A was 0–0, $\therefore$ B v C was 5–5.

C had t goals for and we know that C won their match v D. $\therefore$ score in C v D can only be 1–0, for t cannot be more than 9 ($3+5+1=9$).

A v B:	0–0	B v C:	5–5
A v C:	0–3	C v D:	1–0

(i) They are 'all to play each other once'..∴. no side can have played more than 2 matches. If for any team Pl was 0, then *all* the figures across would be 0, making more than 1 figure correct..∴. each team has played at least once.

(ii) If all Pl's were wrong, correct figures would be 2, 1, 2. But this is not possible for total of matches played must be even..∴. one of Pl's is correct and all other figures are wrong.

(iii) Consider B. If B's figures were all wrong then B would have Pl 1, L at least 1, and Dr at least 1. But this is not possible. ∴. B Pl is correct and all other figures are wrong.

(iv) A's Pl and C's Pl must each be 2; A's W and Dr must each be 1, and A's L is 0. B's L and Dr must each be 1, and B's W is 0. ∴. we have:

A	2	1	0	1
B	2	0	1	1
C	2			

(v) C's W cannot be 0 (figure given), . . in order that total of W's and L's should be equal, C must have W 1 and L 1.

(vi) A v B must have been a Dr; A W their other match (v C) and B L the other match (v C).

(vii) A's total of goals against is not 0 (figure given).
A v B was 1–1 or 0–0. *Suppose* 0–0. Then A v C must be 2–1 (at least 1 goal must be scored against A). But A's goals are *not* 2 (figure given) ∴. A v B was *not* 0–0, ∴. it was 1–1.

(viii) B's goals are not 1 (figure given). B v C (Lost) must be 1–2.

(ix) A's total of goals for is not 2 (figure given). A v C is not 1–0. From C's total of goals against (3), C v A is not ?–2, ∴. C v A can only be 0–3.

A v B:	1–1
A v C:	3–0
B v C:	1–2

	Goals Against	Points
A	5	3
B	6	5
C	0	0
D	7	?

(i)　C cannot have 'no goals against *and* no points' since they have played at least once. So their figures are 'goals against 1, points 0' or 'goals against 0, points 1'. Either way, they have played once and did not score. Note also that A's, B's and D's figures are correct.

(ii)　B must have won 2 matches and drawn 1 to get their 5 points. Therefore they played C. Therefore A and D between them scored at least 6 against B. Since B won 2 and drew 1 and there were no more than 7 goals in any match the scores in B's matches against A and D were (B first) 4–3 or 3–3.

(iii)　A got 3 points, so they played D as well as B, and A must have got 2 points against D and 1 against B. So A *v* B was 3–3. Hence B *v* D was 4–3 and B *v* C was 1–0.

(iv)　A had 5 goals against, 3 by B, ∴ 2 by D.
D had 7 goals against, 4 by B, ∴ 3 by A.

A *v* B:	3–3	A *v* D:	3–2
B *v* C:	1–0	B *v* D:	4–3

It would clearly not be possible to discover the score in each match if C and D have played each other (the score could have been anything).

∴ *C cannot have played D.*

Again it will only be possible to find the score in each match if the figures for C's matches played, won, lost, drawn, etc are the same as D's. For otherwise there could be no reason why the figures for C and D should not be interchanged; but if they are the same it will not matter if they are interchanged. On this assumption, and only on this assumption, it will be 'possible to discover the score in each match'.

A draws 2 matches, A *v* C and A *v* D must both be a draw, and the scores must be the same.

The scores could not be 0–0, for A *v* B would then be 7–5 (too many).

Nor could the scores be 1–1, for A *v* B would then be 5–3 (too many).

Nor could the scores be 3–3, for A had only 5 goals against, not 6.

∴ Scores in A *v* C and in A *v* D were 2–2.

∴ Score in A *v* B was 3–1.

∴ B scored 4 goals *v* C and D (5 minus 1), and B had 2 goals scored against them by C and D (5 minus 3).

. ..Score in B *v* C and B *v* D was 2–1.

A *v* B: 3–1		B *v* C: 2–1
A *v* C: 2–2		B *v* D: 2–1
A *v* D: 2–2		

26 | *The Seven Criminals*

We prove first that no line is completely correct.

If Line 1 is correct, then the constables' scores are

1	7,	5,	1,	2,	3,	2
2	5,	7,	1,	3,	4,	3
3	1,	1,	7,	4,	3,	1
4	2,	3,	4,	7,	1,	1
5	3,	4,	3,	1,	7,	2
6	2,	3,	1,	1,	2,	7

Hence no line has seven correct. No line can have exactly six correct, and so the constables' scores must have been 0, 1, 2, 3, 4, 5.

We next show that P was not the first photograph:

If P is correct in column 1, then line 6 is the line with score 0. Hence T is wrong in column 5 and so R is correct in column 5 (since each column contains its correct answer somewhere). Similarly V is wrong in column 7 and so Q is correct: U is wrong in column 3 and R, Q have been allocated elsewhere. Hence there is no letter for column 3. Therefore P is *not* correct in column 1. So R must be in column 1 and T in column 5, giving

R P - - T - -

We next show that Q is in the seventh photograph:

If Q is not correct in column 7, then V is, and the row with zero score must be 3. But then the order must be

	R P Q S T U V	giving scores	4, 2, 0, 2, 1, 4
or	R P Q U T S V	giving scores	2, 4, 0, 3, 2, 5

Therefore Q is correct in column 7 and we fill in the rest easily to give R P U V T S Q (with scores 1, 2, 3, 0, 4, 5).

 RPUVTSQ

Call the clerks' numbers *pq*, *rs* and *tu* where *pq* and *rs* are chosen from 16, 25, 36, 49, 64 and 81.

∴ *pqrs* is 1616, 1625, 1636, ..., 8149, 8164 or 8181, and is a perfect square.

Examination shows that

$$42^2, 43^2, \ldots \ldots \text{ are bigger than } 1699$$
$$51^2, 52^2, \ldots \ldots \text{ are bigger than } 2599$$
$$61^2, 62^2, \ldots \ldots \text{ are bigger than } 3699$$
$$71^2, 72^2, \ldots \ldots \text{ are bigger than } 4999$$
$$81^2, 82^2, \ldots \ldots \text{ are bigger than } 6499$$

and $$91^2, 92^2, \ldots \ldots \text{ are bigger than } 8199$$

So the only possibility is $41^2 = 1681$ and the three numbers are 16, 41 and 81. So the possible combinations are:

divisible by 41	not divisible by 41
411681	418116
168141	164181
	814116
	811641

Browning knows that his number is not first and this knowledge plus the belief that he knows whether the combination is divisible by 41 uniquely identifies a combination for him.

If his is 81: he cannot make a decision.

If his is 41: he can only make a decision if he thinks that 41 is a factor; so knowing his number is not first he chooses 16 81 41. Therefore the 41 *is* in the third place, but the combination is *not* divisible by 41 and so it is 81 16 41.

If his is 16: similar logic shows that he chooses 41 16 81 and that he should have chosen 81 16 41.

811641

It is possible to decode the message by noting certain common occurrences, but we'll do it via the division sum.

From a knowledge of how long division works, we can fill in the spaces to give

```
           OUSU
      NU )IDEEFD
           NU
          ─────
           URE
           DTE
          ─────
            SHF
            UT0
          ─────
             DFD
             DTE
            ─────
               T
```

It is immediate that $O = 1$, $H = $ zero, and $S \times NU$ is divisible by 10. The different endings of the multiples of NU show that $U \neq 0$ or 5 and so $S = 5$. Then looking at the difference $URE - DTE = SH$ shows that $D = U - 1$. Similarly $SHF - UT0 = DF$ shows that $U = S - 1$. So we get the situation of the second figure. Since $1454 \times 84 = 12\text{----}$, it follows that $N = 9$ and the rest is easily found, and the message decoded.

```
           1454
      N4 )13EEF3
           N4
          ─────
           4RE
           3TE
          ─────
            50F
            4T0
          ─────
             3F3
             3TE
            ─────
               T
```

0	1	2	3	4	5	6	7	8	9
H	O	R	D	U	S	E	T	F	N

Under the fourteenth stone north of the nut tree

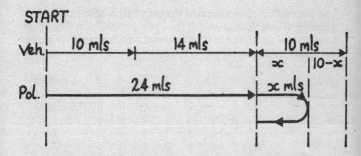

START

Veh. |← 10 mls →|← 14 mls →|← 10 mls →|
                                   x |10−x|

Pol. |← 24 mls →| x mls |

Let x miles be the distance in front of the eventual position of the rear vehicle to the point where the policeman turns.

The column has travelled $14 + x$ miles, while the policeman travelled $24 + x$ miles.

The column has travelled $10 - x$ miles, while the policeman travelled x miles back.

$$\therefore x(14 + x) = (10 - x)(24 + x)$$
$$x^2 + 14x = 120 \text{ miles}. \therefore x = 6 \text{ miles}.$$

The policeman has travelled $24 + 2x = 36$ miles.

36 miles

30 | Fiendish Device

The table below shows some of the early switch changes, and also some involving the last switch (No. 60). 0=OFF, 1=ON. When a switch changes from 1 to 0 the following switch is caused to change over instantaneously.

Switch No.	58	59	60	1	2	3	4	5	Minutes
	0	0	0	1	0	0	0	0	0 (Start)
	0	0	0	0	1	0	0	0	1
	0	0	0	1	1	0	0	0	2
	0	0	0	0	0	1	0	0	3
	0	0	0	1	0	1	0	0	4
	0	0	0	0	1	1	0	0	5
	0	0	0	1	1	1	0	0	6
	0	0	0	0	0	0	1	0	7
	—	—	—	—	—	—	—	—	—
	1	1	1	0	0	1	1	1	n
	1	1	1	1	0	1	1	1	n+1
	1	1	1	0	1	1	1	1	n+2
	1	1	1	1	1	1	1	1	n+3
	0	0	0	0	0	0	0	0	n+4 }
	0	0	0	1	0	0	0	0	n+4 }

Note the chain reaction at, say, the 7th minute; No. 1 changes to OFF, which changes No. 2 to OFF, which changes No. 3 to OFF, which changes No. 4 to ON.

At $(n + 3)$ minutes all 60 switches are set at ON. One minute later a chain reaction occurs as No. 1 goes to OFF; at the end of the chain No. 60, changing to OFF, *immediately* causes No. 1 to change, so that it reverts to ON again.

Things are now as they were at the start, and the process repeats itself ad infinitum. So the requirement for every switch to remain at OFF (that is 0) for 10 seconds simultaneously is never fulfilled.

'Never'

1.   It is evident that the three words (numbers) originally written must have contained 10 letters (all different) and that the only feasible arrangement would be one 4 letter and two 3 letter words (there are, of course, no 2 letter numbers).

2.   As all numbers higher than ten contain more than 4 letters, the only 'possibles' to be considered are one, two, four, five, six, nine and ten and from these the only three having 10 different letters are four, six and ten.

3.   When these three words were converted into 10 different digits and added together, the total ran to five figures. As there was only one four-figure number (and two three-figure numbers) this means that the first figure in the total must be 1 (the highest possible total would be 11,223 made up from say 9,852,741, and 630).

4.   This means that the letter N in NONSO (and in ten) must stand for 1 – and that the letter O can only stand for 0. Thus the total must be 10 1–0.

5.   The perfect square standing for ten must end in the figure 1. The 'possibles' (for ten) to be considered are, therefore, 361 (19^2), 841 (29^2) and 961 (31^2).

6.   As the five-figure total ends in 0, it will be found that the units in the three perfect squares must be 1, 4 and 5 (no perfect square ends in 2, 3, 7 or 8 and any ending in 0 has a second 0, i.e. ends in 00 which is not acceptable).

7.   Three-figure perfect squares to be considered for six are, therefore, 324 (18^2), 625 (25^2) and 784 (28^2).

8.   Combinations possible for ten and six and four are, therefore:

	Ten	Six	Digits for Four
(a)	361	784	0259
(b)	841	625	0379
(c)	961	324	0578
(d)	961	784	0235

Of these, only (a) will be found satisfactory, i.e.:

Ten	361	(19^2)
Six	784	(28^2)
Four	9025	(95^2)
NONSO	10170	

361, 784 and 9025

The given clues are summarised as follows:

(A) Two men, also two women (maiden names) each of Smiths, Jones and Walkers.

(B) Married and engaged pairs, also men and women alternate round table.

(C) Nobody married or engaged to a person of same surname.

(D) Nobody sits opposite a person of same surname.

(E) Alf, with Jill on his left, at table head; Don and Greta at foot.

(F) Ivy and Lena on Alf's side of table; Eddy on Jill's side next to her.

(G) Ivy and Lena have same surname; so do Eddy and Jill; so do Bill and Hilda; and so do Cyril and Greta.

(H) Fred and Lena each sit between a Smith and a Jones.

Tabulating the explicit information from clues (B)(E)(F) and (G), also, from clue (H), deriving Lena's position at (10) below, hence Ivy at (12) below:

(I)   Consider Lena and Ivy. From clues (A) and (G) their surname is either S or W. If S because of clue (H), either Lena would be engaged to a S, or Ivy would be married to a S, prohibited by clue (C). Hence Lena and Ivy are W.

(J)   Consider Fred. From clue (H) he cannot be at positions (9) or (11), therefore must be at (5). Then, from clues (H) and (C) positions (4) and (6) must hold a S and a J respectively; also, in consequence, and from clues (H) and (D), positions (9) and (11) hold S and J respectively. Thus Fred at (5), engaged to a J, and opposite a W, must be S, from clues (C) and (D).

(K)   Consider Greta. From clue (A), Greta must be S, because there are already two W and two J (Jill and either Kate or Hilda at (6)). Hence Cyril is also S (clue (G)), and must be at (9). Then Bill is J at (11), and Hilda is J at (6) (clue (G)). Kate must be S at (4), and Don must be W (clue (A)).

Cyril Smith and Lena Walker
Fred Smith and Hilda Jones

(i) Davis = f; (ii) Armstrong = m; (iii) John on Jones' right; (iv) Mary next-but-one to f. Brown and f. Stevens; (v) Joan opposite m. Evans; (vi) Joan beside Edna; (vii) Fred next to Bill; (viii) Fred next-but-one to f. Stevens; (ix) m. Smith only m. between two f; (x) f. Brown only f between two m; (xi) only two people of the same sex directly opposite each other.

The following lists give the seating in clockwise order beginning arbitrarily. The relevant items of information are given.

POSSIBILITY A (iv) 1 = f. Stevens, 3 = Mary, 5 = f. Brown. (x) 4 = m, 6 = m. (xi) 2 = f, 7 = m, 8 = f. (ix) 4 = m. Smith. (viii) ? = Fred. Statement (iii) now eliminates this possibility, as will be seen if the seating plan is sketched out.

POSSIBILITY B (iv) 1 = f. Brown, 3 = Mary, 5 = f. Stevens. (x) 2 = m, 8 = m. (xi) 4 = f, 6 = f, 7 = m, 8 = m. (ix) 2 = m. Smith. (viii) 7 = Fred. (vii) 8 = Bill, (v) 4 = Joan, 8 = m. Evans. (vi) 5 = Edna, (iii) 2 = John, 3 = Jones. (i) 4 = Davis. (ii) 7 = Armstrong.

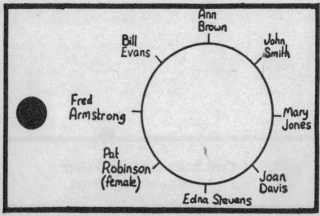

34 | *Prescription Description*

1. From the statements, as Ed has one in common each with Alf and Cyril, he cannot have any in common with Bob and Don.

A and C do not have K(idney) so *B and D must have K.*

2. One person has both H(eart) and S(leeplessness), and it can be A, C or E. *If* A has H and S, E will have H or S, with either N(erves) or I(ndigestion) common to C. C would then have choice of remaining 2nd of N or I, or H or S.

But if C has H/S in common with A, then B and D would be left with the same combination, either KI, or KN, which is not permitted.

As C cannot have N with I, A cannot, therefore, have S with H.

Similar complication occurs if we try C having S with H, so it appears that *E must have S with H.*

3. From here, we can decide that *C and E have S in common* (as cannot have H), also that *S is white. A therefore has H.*

The disposition of N and I cannot now be decided between A, B, C, D without reference to the colour restrictions.

C and D are shown to be only ones to have green (A and B do not and E cannot – 2nd tablet as A), so have their second choice in common, which means that A and B also have 2nd in common.

4. H cannot be yellow (A's statement) or green or white, so must be red or blue.

K cannot be green, yellow or white, so must be red or blue.

N cannot be yellow, white, nor red or blue, so must be green, and so *C and D have N, green.*

I is therefore the only one to be yellow, and is left to A and B.

Now if the H tablets are red, then K is blue. But D cannot have blue with green, so *H must be blue* and *K red.*

Blue
Cyril and Don

Editors' note: The solutions to unscrambling problems are often unilluminating. Readers may find it helpful to write all the pieces of information on separate slips and to try to fit them together as a jig-saw.

(1) From the statements made:
   (a) I lived farther north than W, or, restated, N lives farther
       north than W.
   (b) W lives farther east than M
   (c) M lives farther west than E
   (d) N lived farther east than S
   (e) I may be E, M, or S (but not N or W)
   (f) N turned right to visit E
   (g) I went ahead to visit N

(2) (a) and (b) give possibilities:

```
   N        N        N        N        —        —
 MW—      M—W      —MW      M——      MN—      M—N
   —        —        —        W        W        W
```

Applying (c) gives ten possibilities with E placed (and S in the last place)

```
   N        N        N        N        N
  MWS      MWE      MEW      MSW      MES
  †E       *S        S        E       †W


   N        E        S        E        S
  MSE      MNS      MNE      MSN      MEN
  *W       †W       *W        W        W
```

(3) From (e) try I as E, M and S in turn. Only those marked * satisfy
(d) with I = E and N interchanged; those marked † satisfy (d) with I =
S and N interchanged; none work with I = S. So the possible
situations *before* the move are as shown on the next page, with I in
bold print:

	S	E	E	S	E	S
	MWN	MWN	MEN	MSN	MSN	MEN
	E	S	W	W	W	W
(f)	x	✓	x	✓	✓	x
(g)	x	x	x	x	✓	✓

●   E MNS W   **I am South**

36 | *A Cake Mix*

Given the following facts:

D			sausage
E	lemon		
F			shrimp
G			sausage
H			

(no cheese, egg, coffee)
(no egg)

And, choc cake with cheese, coffee cake with ham but not cheese, choc drink with lemon cake, tea with cheese, no coffee drink for cheese with egg, no shrimp with egg, one only shrimp with lemon.

Also D and G have to have one orange item.

So D does not drink coffee, or lemon, or tea (no cheese), and cannot have choc (as would then have lemon cake) so must have orange.

Similarly the only cake remaining for her must be plain sponge.

As E does not have egg, and D, F and G already have one allotted savoury, only H can have cheese with egg, and so does not drink coffee.

As D has the orange drink, G must have orange cake.

We now have:

D	orange	plain	sausage	
E	lemon			
F			shrimp	
G		orange	sausage	
H			cheese	egg

Now only F or H can have choc drink (with lemon cake). If F, then G must have coffee and H tea. H must also have choc cake, and E coffee cake, also ham. E cannot have egg, cheese or sausage (two gone) with ham, so must have shrimp. But F already has lemon (cake) with shrimp, so we come to a dead end.

If H has choc drink, and F coffee and G tea, then F choc cake and E coffee cake. But both F (choc cake) and G (tea drinker) require cheese, and one already gone to H.

So, if H has choc drink, F must have tea, and G coffee. F then has choc cake and cheese. E is left with coffee cake.

We now have:

D	orange	plain	sausage	
E	lemon	coffee	ham	
F	tea	choc	cheese	shrimp
G	coffee	orange	sausage	
H	choc	lemon	cheese	egg

E cannot have egg or cheese, sausage has gone, so must have shrimp. D cannot have egg, so must have ham, and G has egg.

Dot and Eve

The shortest route from N to Q passes L and one other plant. So they must be as shown:

The (direct) route M→T→S cannot avoid *both* the junctions ■; and the route from P to N passes one other plant (not R, S or T). So we must place P as shown (or the equivalent position below):

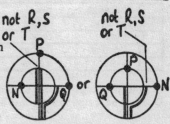

The only possible positions for the route M→T→S are shown — above. But if M is on the diameter through NQ then wherever you try to place O it is clear that the route from O to M does not pass R, S or T (contradicting the given information). Hence M must be at an end of one of the — but not on the diameter NQ, giving possibilities:

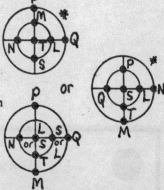

In * it is impossible to place O
satisfying the fact that it is over
twice as far from O to M when
you have to avoid R, S and T.
So in the remaining figure we
place O (and hence the others)
to give the layout shown. The
required route from N to M is
marked.

Orpine, Polyanthus and Quitch

38 | Round the Pond

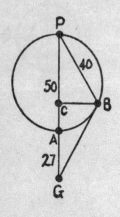

The first approximation to a solution is found by assuming that Boris' route with his boat is the straight line BG.

angle PBA = 90° (semicircle)
PA = 50, PB = 40, so AB = 30

Draw BC perpendicular to PA. Then

$$\frac{BC}{BA} = \frac{PB}{PA} = \frac{4}{5} \text{ and } BC = \frac{4}{5}.30 = 24.$$

Similarly CA = 18 and CG = 45 giving

$$BG = \sqrt{BC^2 + CG^2} = \sqrt{24^2 + 45^2} = 51$$

Boris' boat reaches B in 120 seconds; Arthur's reaches A in 150. Boris runs BG in $\frac{4}{3} \times 51 = 68$ seconds; Arthur runs AG in 36.

So (it seems) that Boris takes 188 seconds, Arthur 186 and that Arthur wins by 2 seconds.

However, if you draw the situation to scale (or do something more mathematical like finding out where the tangents from G touch the circle) you will see that the straight-line route BG actually goes through the water! The actual shortest route on land from B to G is

$$\frac{5\pi}{36} \times (180 - 2\sin^{-1}\frac{4}{5} - \cos^{-1}\frac{25}{52}) + \sqrt{52^2 - 25^2}!!$$

As the picture suggests, this is *very* little farther (3·9 centimetres), and the required answer is unaffected.

 Arthur by 2 seconds

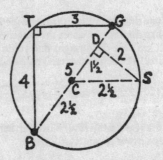

If one unit = distance swum by goldfish in 15 minutes, then its route is BT (4) and TG (3), and it ends up diametrically opposite from where it started (5 units away).

The shubunkin's route is

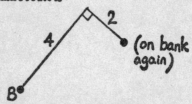

and, as can be seen from the first figure, this can only fit in as shown (B→D→S). Therefore the shubunkin's longest possible straight swim is along the obvious diameter.

 Due west

There were nine different answers given, and the maximum number of handshakes for any person is eight. So the answers given were 0–8 inclusive.

The 10 people are labelled by their answers, and two will be joined by a line if they shook hands.

8 must be joined to everyone except 0.

So 1 shakes only 8's hand, and 7 must be joined to everyone except 0 and 1.

So 2 shakes only 8's and 7's hands, and 6 must be joined to everyone except 0, 1 and 2.

And so on.

This eventually gives:

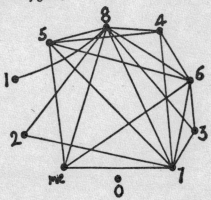

Also note that 8, 0 are married; hence 7, 1 are married; hence 6, 2 are married, 5, 3 are married, and my wife is 4. Therefore my wife and I shake precisely the same hands, and the only women amongst them is Mrs A. So my wife shakes hands with Mrs A, Mr B, Mr C and Mr D.

continued overleaf

The sum of 0, 1, 2, 3, 4, 5, 6, 7 and 8 is 36 and so the four other men shake 18 hands in total. But I shake 5, 6, 7, and 8, which includes three of these men. But any three of these add to at least 18 and so the men are 0, 5, 6 and 7; and Mrs A is 8.

Mrs A, Mr B, Mr C and Mr D
8

Four of the correct 3-by-3 squares must come from the corners of the original 5-by-5. We consider the colours on the central cross shown. For example *abc* could be BBB, in which case, trying to fit all the 3-by-3s in turn into the bottom right-hand corner, we see that *ade* would have to be BWW or BWB as follows:

We write
3
BBB———→BWW

We write
2
BBB———→BWB

Now to fill in four 3-by-3s in the corners is equivalent to going right round in this fashion and finding four such links which fit together thus (with four different numbers alongside)

e.g.

$$\text{→BBB} \xrightarrow{2} \text{BWB} \xrightarrow{4} \text{BWW} \xrightarrow{6} \text{BBW}$$
3

continued overleaf

A diagram showing all these arrows is as follows:

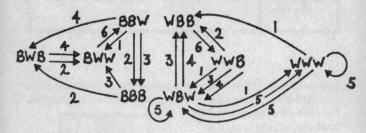

The only routes of the required type are

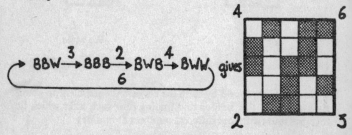

In each case we can construct the corresponding 5-by-5. For example

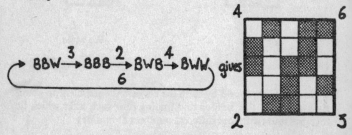

But in this example it is impossible to fit either of the remaining 1 and 5. However in just one of the cases, namely

it is possible to fit 2 correctly and 3 with one square changed (and not in one of the four corners). Since 3 was the right way up, the answer is as shown below (with 3 in the centre).

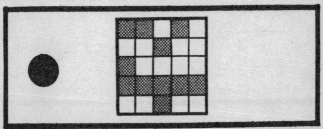

Editors' note: Readers will probably have tried this one as an unusual jigsaw. The above solution is included as an outline of a more mathematical approach.

As the sexes are equally divided and the teacher is a man, the middle row is girl, boy, girl.

Every digit is used once and so the scores were 2,3,4,5,6,7,8,9 and 10. These have sum 54 and will form a Magic Square with row-sum 18.

The central digit must be 6. (For the sum of the central row, central column, and two diagonals is 72 and this must be 54 plus three times the centre.) Now 2 cannot be in a corner because there are insufficient large numbers to make up its three rows etc. to 18. Also, obviously, 4 cannot be in a line with 2. So the four corners are 3,5,7 and 9.

Mirror images (left to right) are not relevant to this puzzle, so we give below the four relevant possibilities, with the top row being the front of the class:

	A			B			C			D	
9	2	7	5	4	9	3	10	5	7	8	3
4	6	8	10	6	2	8	6	4	2	6	10
5	10	3	3	8	7	7	2	9	9	4	5

As no girl gets less than three marks, *A*, *B* and *D* are ruled out. In *C* the highest mark awarded to a boy is 9.

Since V = 2G and Y − W = W − V, both V and Y are even. Since Y is top, Y = 24 and the marks are 0, 1, 2, . . ., 24 with a row-sum of 60.

Y = 24, H = 23, J = 22 and F + G + I = 60 − 23 − 22 = 15.

I (= 4F) must be 4, 8 or 12 but since G is odd the only possibility is F = 2, I = 8, G = 5 and V (= 2G) = 10, W (= Y − ½ (Y − V)) = 17, M (= G + (Y − W)) = 12, S = 19.

So the square is as shown below, with numbers as yet unused being 0, 1, 3, 4, 6, 7, 9, 11, 13, 14, 15, 16, 18, 20, 21.

A	B	C	D	E
F	G	H	I	J
2	5	23	8	22
K	L	M	N	O
		12		
P	Q	R	S	T
			19	
U	V	W	Y	Z
	10	17	24	

In the third row C + R = 8, which must be 7 + 1 and since C > R we have C = 7, R = 1. In the bottom line U + Z = 9 which must be 0 + 9 or 3 + 6. But U > Z and Z ≠ 0 (for that would make A = 24 = Y). Hence U = 6, Z = 3, A = 21. In the fourth row 0 + 9 is needed for D + N. D = 9 is impossible in the first line (for no numbers are available to make B + E = 23) and so D = 0, N = 9. Similarly the remainder of the square can be filled-in: the top row gives B = 14, E = 18: the E/U diagonal gives Q = 16: the second row gives L = 15. Since O + T = 17 and O + K = 24 and O < K the remaining numbers can be distributed to give O = 4, T = 13, P = 11, K = 20 and K − O = 16.

Kenneth beat Olga by 16 marks

44 | *Classier Magic*

	2x−1	
	x	
	1	

Possible values (excluding non-primes in x and 2x−1 columns below):

		Row	
x	2x−1	Total	
3	5	9	a
7	13	21	b
19	37	57	c
31	61	93	d
37	73	111	e
.	.	.	.
.	.	.	.
.	.	.	.
too big	.	.	

a and *b* are NOT possible as there are not enough different primes to fill the squares.
If *c*, then top line has 37 in middle, leaving 20 to be made up.
Only primes are 3/17 and 7/13. 3/17 means that one diagonal totals 3+19+35; 35 non-prime. 7/13 means diagonal 13+19+25 again NOT prime.

So we are left with *d* and *e* . . .

If *d*, top line has 61 in middle, so that 32 has to be made up to give total of 93.

Only possibilities are 3/29 and 13/19

3/29 makes one diagonal 29+31+33 NOT prime

13/19 makes one diagonal 13+31+49 NOT prime

so d is out.

If *e*, top line has 73 in middle leaving 38 to complete 111. This CAN be done with 31/7 (or 7/31).

Middle line has 37 with 13 and 61

Bottom line has 67 with 1 and 43

All lines give total 111. So this is the SMALLEST total, the one we seek. Third largest number is 61 and, as it cannot be on the right, the answer follows:

7	73	31
61	37	13
43	1	67

45 | *Powerless*

Call the two numbers A (the larger) and B (the smaller). $kA+B$ is never divisible by A and so never a power of A. (However it can be a power of B:

$$\text{e.g.} \quad 243 = 3^5 = 48 \cdot 5 + 3.)$$

In the following table we give, for each A and B allowed, the number of A's which when added to B give a power of B:

A \ B	2	3	4	5	6	7
3	2	—	—	—	—	—
4	—	6	—	—	—	—
5	6	48	12	—	—	—
6	—	—	2	20	—	—
7	2	312	36	11160	30	—
8	—	3	—	15	??	42

e.g. when A=3 and B=2, $2.A+B=2^3$ so we enter 2 in the table. Similarly when A=4 and B=3, $6.A+B=3^3$.

So the only possibility is A=8 and B=6. We must check that these *do* work.

$k.8+6$ is clearly never a power of 2, 3, 4, 5, 7, 8 or 9, for $k.8+6$ is even but not divisible by 8. And 6^3, 6^4, 6^5, ... are all divisible by 8.

8 and 6

46 | *Just the Ticket*

Firstly the tickets must be consecutively numbered:

either $a, b, c, d,$ and $a, b, c, d+1$ where $a, b, c, d, d+1$ are digits.

If my answer to the question about the total on one ticket being thirteen had been yes then all my wife could glean would be that $a+b+c+d=12$ and regardless of the answer to the next question could not have ascertained the individual numbers.

If my answer to that question had been no then the above statement of numbers format is not correct.

or $a, b, c, 9$ and $a, b, c+1, 0$ are the numbers.

Thus $2a+2b+2c+10=25$ so $a+b+c=7\frac{1}{2}$ which is impossible as this must be an integer.

or $a, b, 9, 9$ and $a, b+1, 0, 0$ are the numbers.

Thus $2a+2b+19=25$ so $a+b=3$. This leads to the following possibilities:

	a	b	Numbers	Answers	
(i)	0	3	0399 and 0400	Yes	No
(ii)	1	2	1299 and 1300	No	No
(iii)	2	1	2199 and 2200	Yes	No
(iv)	3	0	3099 and 3100	Yes	No

Only in (ii) above is there no third appearance of any digit. If my answer to the question about any digit appearing more than twice had been yes then there is no unique solution. So my answer to this must also have been no for my wife to state the numbers in (ii) above.

or $a, 9, 9, 9$ and $a+1, 0, 0, 0$ are the numbers

Thus $2a+28=25$ which is impossible, as a cannot be negative, let alone fractional.

1299 and 1300

	has initially	*spends*	*has left*
Anne	A	A_1	A_2
Betty	B	B_1	B_2
Carole	C	C_1	C_2

where (A, B, C), (A_1, B_1, C_1), (A_2, B_2, C_2) are groups of 3-digit numbers containing the nine positive digits. Further

$$C = A + B, \quad A = A_1 + A_2, \quad B = B_1 + B_2, \quad C = C_1 + C_2,$$
$$A > B, \quad C_1 = 3C/5, \quad A_1 \text{ slightly greater than } 3A/5.$$

It is known that C is a multiple of 9, it is also a multiple of 5; thus C is an odd multiple of 45. But C must certainly exceed 500 and contain distinct digits. Hence C = 675, 765 or 945. But $C_2 = 2C/5 = 270$, 306 or 378. Hence $C_2 = 378$, C = 945, $C_1 = 567$.

Since $A > B > 200$ there are four solutions of $C = A + B$;

$$945 = 628 + 317 = 627 + 318 = 618 + 327 = 617 + 328.$$

We now take each of these four solutions in turn and attempt to complete the matrix above with all conditions satisfied. The reasoning is straightforward.

A	628	382	246	627	382	245	618	3--	2--	617	3--	2--
B	317	1--	1--	318	149	169	327	1--	1--	328	1--	1--
C	945	567	378	945	567	378	945	567	378	945	567	378

There remains just one solution.

Anne £2.45
Betty £1.69
Carole £3.78

To have any chance of satisfying the given conditions each mouse must be able to reach 4 or 5 squares of his own cage (a 4-type or a 5-type, say). Each 5-type must have a wall at *dh* or *ef*, and so there is at most one 5-type. If the three cages are 4-type, 4-type and 5-type, then for some 4/5 combination a mouse from a 4-type must be able to reach more squares than the mouse from the 5-type. This is soon seen to be impossible.

So all three cages are 4-types.

i.e.: one of 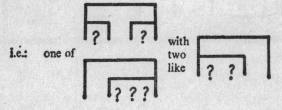 with two like

But then the three are soon seen to be

Astoria   Dorchester   Hilton

continued overleaf

Now

For 'A>D'   For 'D>H'   For 'H>A'

Dorchester   Hilton

The sum of the numbers 1–12 is 78.

There are three distinct quartets of hours, and if their sums are equal, then the sum of each is 26.

The two such quartets with the lowest products are:

1	2	11	12	product = 264
1	3	10	12	360

and the two with the highest products are:

4	6	7	9	1512
5	6	7	8	1680

all other combinations having products between 360 and 1512.

The *only* pair of quartets for which the product for one is greater than six times that of the other is:

	1	2	11	12	call it A
and	5	6	7	8	call it B

and so the third is:

3	4	9	10	call it C

A is determined since Johnny got 12 right: i.e.

Hour	Counter
3	1
6	2
9	11
12	12

continued overleaf

(remembering that each quartet's numbers increase in the clock-wise direction).

We then have:

The Two Remaining Quartets of Hours		Four Possible Arrangements of B's Counters				Ditto for C			
X	Y	B1	B2	B3	B4	C1	C2	C3	C4
1	2	5	8	7	6	3	10	9	4
4	5	6	5	8	7	4	3	10	9
7	8	7	6	5	8	9	4	3	10
10	11	8	7	6	5	10	9	4	3

The total of 32 possible arrangements is distributed as follows:

No. of correct hours (excluding 12)	Arrangements		No.
0	(B2, B3, B4) in X	and (C1, C2, C3, C4) in Y	12
	(B1, B3) in Y	and (C2, C3, C4) in X	6
1	(B1) in X	and (C1, C2, C3, C4) in Y	4
	(B2, B4) in Y	and (C2, C3, C4) in X	6
2	(B1, B3) in Y	and (C1) in X	2
3	(B2, B4) in Y	and (C1) in X	2
			32

Since 12 was not the only correct counter, we disregard the zero number. If Jill were to tell her colleague that there were 1 or 3 correct hours, then Mary would not be able to say uniquely which were correct.

But for 2 correct hours, the hours are unique.

Hence (C1) in X gives 4 and 10 correctly placed.

4 and 10

Let Y be the highest-numbered button which takes the lift as high or higher than expected.

Write $x \to y$ to mean that button x takes you to floor y.

If $x \to y$ where $x \leqslant y$, then $(x-1) \to z$ where $x-1 \leqslant z$. (For *otherwise* the milkman would travel from y to z after pushing button $x-1$ taking him from above floor $x-1$ to below it.)

So if button x takes you as high or higher than expected, then so does button $x-1$.

BUTTONS	BUTTONS
0, 1, 2, . . ., Y	Y+1, Y+2, . . ., 9
take you as high or	take you lower than
higher than expected	expected

But three of $1 \to 2$, $2 \to 4$, $3 \to 6$, $4 \to 8$ hold. Also $0 \to 0$, and $e \to e$ for the electrician's floor. So $Y \geqslant 4$, and the two buttons of the form $x \to \dfrac{x}{2}$ must be $6 \to 3$ and $8 \to 4$. So button 6 takes you lower than expected and Y=4 or 5.

Let $1 \to x$. Then some other button leads to x and this is the only repeated floor. So as $8 \to 4$ it follows that $2 \nrightarrow 4$, $4 \nrightarrow 4$ and $5 \nrightarrow 4$. So the three doubling buttons are $1 \to 2$, $3 \to 6$ and $4 \to 8$.

Now $Y \to Y$ or $(Y+1) \to Y$ (for otherwise after pushing button Y he will pass right past floor Y). Since $4 \nrightarrow 4$ and $5 \nrightarrow 4$ it follows that Y=5 and the rest can be filled in without too much trouble to give $0 \to 0$, $1 \to 2$, $2 \to 9$, $3 \to 6$, $4 \to 8$, $5 \to 5$, $6 \to 3$, $7 \to 2$, $8 \to 4$, $9 \to 7$.

7, 4, 2, 3, 5, 8, 6, 9

List of Authors

1. G. H. Dickson
2. Ronald Postill
3. Brig. A. G. H. Brousson
4. B. T. Izzard
5. Victor Bryant
6. J. S. Rowley
7. G. H. Dickson
8. P. Hayward
9. G. H. Dickson
10. Arthur Adams
11. R. A. England
12. John Halsall
13. N. A. Phillips
14. Sir Brian Young
15. D. C. Pusinelli
16. Eric Emmet
17. Eric Emmet
18. J. H. Perryman
19. Ronald Postill
20. Arthur Adams
21. J. P. Mernagh
22. Eric Emmet
23. Eric Emmet
24. Eric Emmet
25. Eric Emmet
26. Robert Gray
27. J. E. Kessel & J. R. Partridge
28. Eric Emmet
29. Lt-Gen. Sir John Cowley G.C.
30. Lt-Col. C. E. Booth-Jones
31. J. L. Bowles
32. J. S. P. Roberton
33. A. W. Gebbie
34. Mary Connor
35. J. S. P. Roberton
36. Mary Connor
37. Victor Bryant
38. Ronald Postill
39. Sir Brian Young
40. D. Preston
41. A. K. Austin
42. Gerald Fitzgibbon
43. Alfred Moritz
44. Ronald Postill
45. Richard Furner
46. D. Poulter
47. Rhombus
48. A. K. Austin
49. Bryan Thwaites
50. Victor Bryant